In the whirlwind that swept over the Vietnam quagmire, many observers themselves inadvertently became part of the situation by keeping their own biased viewpoints. Ngo The Vinh was fully involved, and his book lets us face all the facts.

—MAC DO
author of *The Fortieth*

I am impressed with the knowledge, foresight and sympathy that Ngo The Vinh displays in The Green Belt, *which he wrote more than thirty years ago. Although the book is a piece of fiction, many of the events alluded to are historical. The dynamics and dilemmas depicted were real dilemmas for various parties involved and especially for the Thuong (highland) people, who are portrayed as victims of various policies and conflicts.*

—DR. OSCAR SALEMINK
Free University, Amsterdam
author of *The Ethnography of Vietnam's Central Highlanders*

It's fiction with true feelings and engaged compassion. It invites the readers to plunge into the undisclosed twist-and-turn details. This fascinating story presents an insightful, moving, and sensitive look at what destructive emotions did to a country and its minority ethnic groups.

—DR. PHONG T. NGUYEN
Ethnomusicologist and NEA National Heritage Fellow

I read The Green Belt *with great interest. It brought back memories of the Central Highlands in the 1960s and the events surrounding the Buddhist and student unrest during that period.*

It's clear that Ngo The Vinh learned a great deal about the highland people and their plight during the war and post-war world. What news I now get from the highlands is very sad. The Montagnards are facing a worse threat to their way of life than at any time previously. The Americans (like the French) used the Montagnards and coldly abandoned them. All one can do is to keep trying to bring it to the attention of American leaders in Washington. Still one hopes against hope.

—DR. GERALD C. HICKEY
author of *Window On a War: An Anthropologist in the Vietnam conflict*

THE GREEN BELT

ERESE L. WRIGHT

; Best wishes

03 / 2005

NGO THE VINH

THE GREEN BELT

A NOVEL

NGO THE VINH

Translated from the Vietnamese by
Nha Trang & William L. Pensinger

Ivy House
Publishing Group
www.ivyhousebooks.com

Also by Ngo The Vinh:

The Battle of Saigon

The Mekong River Drained Dry,
 South China Sea in Turmoil

PUBLISHED BY IVY HOUSE PUBLISHING GROUP
5122 Bur Oak Circle, Raleigh, North Carolina 27612
United States of America
919-782-0281
www.ivyhousebooks.com

ISBN 1-57197-394-X
Library of Congress Control Number: 2003094453

Printed in the United States of America

For Sons of the Mountains,
who have been there from the beginning.

CONTENTS

FOREWORD

The Green Belt begins with a young Vietnamese painter-turned-journalist's disillusion of reality limiting his parameters to ridiculous confines, and ends with his firsthand experience about an uncertain future of the ethnics on the Vietnamese highlands. All was subject to war plans that were in reality the spoils of ideology.

All wars ultimately reveal the hidden motives of the policy-makers, which are fascinating and subject to endless investigations due to their complexities. Therefore, the anatomy of a war would require a method of deconstruction, revealing more doubts, and possibly ending with irresolvable dilemma.

Some wars, like the one in Vietnam, were shrouded in a sort of mystification, or they were cleverly mystified, so deep and "exegetated" that many who fought in such wars misperceived the many facets of the reasons for fighting and became confused by them. They were enmeshed in an ideological game that expected them to act and think instinctively but not reflectively, or not teleologically.

This condition is exactly what was described in tableaux of *The Green Belt*. War games have been classically characterized by archetypes, the good and the bad. Without this antagonism there would be no war, and no cause at all to fight. Being "good" perhaps means to be trustful or to be exact. In the case of the Vietnam War, the good must be a *savior* who comes to liberate victims from the hands of dictator.

Perhaps this has been also true for many ethnics on the Vietnamese highlands. Standing in front of a Frenchman and a Vietnamese, the highland native would have no trust in the latter. Simply, during the French colonial times, a Frenchman was rich, and a Vietnamese not only poor but a second-class citizen in his very homeland.

If a highland native in Vietnam needed a savior, only the French was considered a true liberator in his stead at the door. In reality, the French was no savior. His presence on the highlands confirmed his sovereignty over the colony in which all ethnics must not trust each other. He did not come as a liberator, but a ruler to exploit other races and their lands. Why did he look so terrific? Simply, he had wealth and power.

During the Vietnam War, the American replaced the French image to continue the discourse, the Face. The American presence on the Vietnamese highlands was significant because of Communist terrorism. The difference was ideology. In praxis, the Communists ruled by terrors, allowing their own kind no time to reflect on subject matter, and no chance to pass judgments, save accepting their guidelines and ultimatums. The highland ethnics in Vietnam never had been considered as human beings. South Vietnamese troops were called on not to protect such innocents, but to stop North Vietnamese infiltration, a job that could never have materialized without the deployment of American Green Berets and Washington advisors.

At least, the coalition showed that the highlanders were no "barbarians" or *mọi* in Vietnamese language and belief. They could be used for intelligence networks and recruited to fight against North Vietnam in a war that surpassed all conventional boundaries, within which unfortunately existed their homelands. They would be *de jure* Vietnamese American allies; *de facto*, they were not an equal part, still looking for trust and protection. Who would be their defender? The Vietnamese or the American? Words are rhetorical before situational, exigencies in which facts were the only measure of trust. Therefore, the massacre of some hundred Thuong or highlanders instantiated in *The Green Belt* was in fact the effect of a well-scripted drama. It was played for the Thuong to determine for themselves the true liberator or savior they would need. But the choice had never been that simple.

After the Paris Accord came Vietnamization, by which Washington could wash its hands and depart in an orderly fashion from South Vietnam, because the game was moving to an end. If South Vietnamese people were abandoned, what would become of the highlanders in Vietnam? Once they belonged to the margins of history, they would remain there invisibly and begin to think about their "savior," their loss, and especially their uncertain future.

The problems confronting the Vietnamese people must be handled by the Vietnamese. Similarly, what concerns the existence of the highland ethnics in Vietnam must be resolved among and by themselves. There is no outside "savior"; so remarked Emmanuel Lévinas, in a different historical environment, when the philosopher was consulted for his advice to end the sufferings of people, victims of the corrupt systems in Latin America.

Perhaps for hundreds of years, the highland ethnics in Vietnam had believed they were safe at home—separately from the Vietnamese in the lowland, politically, culturally, socially, and economically. From their point of view, the power conflicts between Vietnamese people as well as between Vietnamese people and their invaders had never affected their way of life. This was not so until the establishment of the French Indochina, and especially during the Vietnam War.

In that war, especially at the time significantly marked by the escalation of American involvement, the South Vietnamese government did not have a clear focus, which was true even to all South Vietnamese people. This fact is clearly discussed in *The Green Belt;* the novel won the National Prize for Literature yet ironically saw its author in court contradictory to the governmental institution that recognized its contribution and merit.

Thirty years since the first publication of *Vòng Đai Xanh,* the original title in Vietnamese version in Saigon, Dr. Ngo The Vinh has republished it in America, for he believes that the margins of history, metaphorically speaking, or the fate of the Highlanders in Vietnam deserve Vietnamese and international attention. To make this a matter of human conscience, the author needs an English version available for an international audience.

I owe to Nha Trang and William L. Pensinger the honor they have given me of reading every chapter of their English translation since the inception of the project. *The Green Belt* is a super work, not because the translators have linguistically succeeded in transmitting the substance from one language to another, but also clarified concepts and terminologies that could be impossible without solid knowledge and experience of Vietnamese culture, language, and the experience of Vietnam War. This task is not easy, although we know the translators are also scholars and writers whose exhaustive novel *The Moon of Hòa-Bình,* a highly challenging work with strong visionary concept, posits a different mode of thinking and seeing.

I would like to thank Dr. Vinh for his confidence in my knowledge to write this foreword for his novel, a job I have found myself incapable of regarding the book's details, but leave them to the readers' discretions and discoveries of the text and contexts of this fine novel. From this point, I would ruffle up the fine volume, to share first with him and then with the readers my sympathy, *"to transform into reality the vision of the highlands as a Promised land was a task that would take 'longer than raising a cup of rice wine to your lips'—as a* Thuong *idiomatic expression goes—a long and arduous task entailing much more blood, sweat, and tears."* This very vision remains a tragedy for the ethnics on the Vietnamese Central Highlands and the Vietnamese today, but *The Green Belt* is one important action towards fulfilling this task.

—Dr. Nguyen Quynh
Towson University, Maryland
Spring 2003

PREFACE

to the 1986 Vietnamese language edition,
entitled *Vòng Đai Xanh*

A painful, bitter page of history, thought to have been forgotten, was evoked anew when in November 1986, more than two hundred Thuong persons boarded an airplane to fly from a transit camp in the Philippines to Los Angeles International Airport, en route to their new resettlement area in North Carolina. In the end, they left behind the devastating Vietnam War, a protracted war awash in bloodshed, suffering, and heavy losses of all kinds.

Thuong is the collective name used to refer to approximately thirty indigenous tribal groups who live in the Central Highlands of Vietnam. They speak many different languages and wear different types of clothes, maintain tribal rites and rituals, and engage in distinct customs and practices; their livelihood depends essentially on swidden rice cultivation using the slash-and-burn method, as well as on hunting.

Before the war, it can accurately be said, Thuong highlanders led a life separate from that of lowland Vietnamese, or Kinh. But their peaceful existence was all but terminated following the

Second World War. They were decisively impacted by the contemporary outside world for the first time during the nine years of the First Indochina War (1945–54) between the French and the Vietnamese. That war ended with the defeat of the French. The Geneva Accords of 1954 divided Vietnam into two parts, and governing of the whole of the Central Highlands, with its Thuong population of almost one million people, was handled by the Saigon government of South Vietnam.

Aware of the high level of strategic importance of this mountainous region, during the first few months after the Geneva Accords, the Saigon government engaged in one attempt after another to assimilate the Thuong peoples, as well as other ethnic minorities, into Vietnamese society, without any consideration for their unique traditional cultures. In accordance with the Dinh Điền policy of the Diem regime—the migration and resettlement program whose aim was to move people into undeveloped "public domain" where they would clear and claim land—tens of thousands of Vietnamese Catholic refugees from North Vietnam were sent to settle in the Central Highlands, encroaching on fertile lands that had long been the home of the Thuong peoples, had long been their property. Added to this violation were other misguided decisions: closing traditional law courts run according to Thuong customs, banning highlander languages, and setting limitations upon Thuong representatives in administrative structures. It was not hard to understand the resulting resentment, uncooperativeness, and even opposition on the part of the Thuong.

In the early 1960s, along with the increase in America's direct involvement in the Vietnam War, the situation of the highlanders radically changed. Indeed, Thuong people welcomed the Americans with open arms, and subsequently mutual attachment and ties were developed between the two parties. American advisors needed help from the Thuong to gather intelligence on the movement and infiltration of the communists. For their part, the

Thuong believed that their American friends would protect them from the threats posed by both the Vietnamese nationalists and their enemy—the communists—and that furthermore the Americans would guarantee Thuong autonomy once the war ended.

During both Indochina Wars, Thuong people were victims caught in the cross fire of opposing forces. When one compares the destructive effects of the First Indochina War on the life of the highlanders with those of the Second Indochina War—during which more advanced modern firepower was utilized by both sides—it is beyond doubt that in the latter case the Thuong had to pay a dearer price, suffering heavier losses than did all sides actively involved as contenders in the conflict. In fact, when the war had escalated beyond the guerrilla warfare stage, the fate of the Thuong received very little attention. In order to prevent North Vietnamese troops from infiltrating the highlands along the Ho Chi Minh Trail, American jet fighters and B-52 bombers day and night carpet bombed the whole mountainous region. In addition, the toxic defoliant Agent Orange, which the Americans sprayed over the highlands, inflicted extremely severe damage to Thuong people. With the Tet Offensive of 1968 and the Summer Offensive of 1972, the highlands were sunk deeper into war and death. The communist army did not hesitate to use destructive weapons like grenades and flamethrowers to attack mountainous villages and hamlets, which were surrounded by fragile fences for defense. Highland social structures almost completely collapsed, and the so-called map of the ethnic groups' locations was no longer of any value. Around 1972, the American military estimated that about two hundred thousand Thuong people had perished in the war, and 85 percent of traditional mountainous villages were completely wiped out.

The Paris Peace Accords signed in January 1973, which prepared for the United States to withdraw its troops from Vietnam, merely began the Vietnamization stage of the war, rather than ending it altogether. Under the changed circumstance, Thuong's lives were even more severely afflicted, this time by the remaining two Vietnamese sides fighting each other for territory and for people's allegiance.

At the end of 1974, the political and military situation in South Vietnam further deteriorated. Thuong leaders well realized that they could not depend on the Saigon government for anything. They began to panic when the staff of the American Embassy left Vietnam. According to a 1986 report from Josh Jetlin, the *Los Angeles Times* correspondent, these Thuong leaders had implored the American officials to help them escape from the country, for fear that they and their families would be imprisoned and murdered if left behind. But they never received such help. In the meantime, a few other Thuong persons were trying to seek military support from the Americans for their continued struggle in the deep jungle, in anticipation of the collapse of the Saigon government. The answer they received from various American officials was something to this effect: they, the Americans, needed time to consider the request before they could give a definite answer. Because they did not understand the subtlety of diplomatic language, these Thuong people were not aware that their entreaty in actuality had been rejected.

The beginning of March 1975 marked the loss of the hill resort, Ban Me Thuot, because of a strategic bungle of fatal proportions made by South Vietnamese generals when they abandoned this mountainous region. A bloody evacuation along the national highway ensued, which propelled the complete disintegration of the Saigon government. Thus, the most agonizing fear of the Thuong turned into reality: the communist government was subsequently established in the South. Thousands of the Thuong were sent to reeducation camps, a number of their leaders executed, and inhabitants of mountainous villages and hamlets were tightly checked and controlled because they were suspected of having fought on the side of the Americans. A few of them sought freedom in the deep jungle, taking up arms to resist the new government. Also, according to Jetlin, because Hanoi had greater firepower, the Thuong suffered severe losses. They had to leave Vietnam and take refuge in Laos. Subsequently, again being surrounded by communist troops, they had to cross hundreds of miles to reach Cambodia, where they were confronted with the Khmer Rouge. At first, the Thuong naively believed that because they all shared the goal of fighting against the Vietnamese, the Khmer Rouge would assist them. But it actually turned out that the Khmer Rouge were suspicious of them too, and placed them in a concentration camp deep inside Cambodian territory. Exhausted after all their armed struggle, they only waited for an opportunity to flee and seek refuge in Thailand. The lucky opportunity presented itself in the winter of 1984 when the Vietnamese communist army heavily shelled Khmer Rouge camps, which inadvertently opened the way for the Thuong to escape from confinement. What followed was a migration on foot, without a map, without any weapons, involving women and children. But, finally, they made it to the Thai border.

After countless interventions and bureaucratic procedures, eventually this group of 213 Thuong persons were allowed to settle in the United States. They arrived at the time of Thanksgiving celebration. To the American people, Thanksgiving this year had an added meaning, for it extended its grace to embrace these new immigrants from the deep mountains and jungles of mainland Southeast Asia. Not only were these immigrants devastated by the war, but they could also be seen as pitiful survivors from oppression and cruel discrimination meted out to them by Vietnamese of opposing sides.

Sixteen years after its first publication in Saigon, against the background of the first celebration of Thanksgiving for the

Thuong, it was suggested by the publisher and friends that the novel *Vòng Đai Xanh, The Green Belt,* be reprinted in California. The main purpose of the reprint is no other than to recollect and reflect on an incomplete first chapter of a voluminous book yet to be written, a chapter that deals with the forgotten war in the Central Highlands involving the Thuong people's struggle and heartrending experience, a forgotten war within the protracted and complex Second Indochina War during a divisive period of Vietnamese history, which was marked with innumerable forms of disintegration, at which time even truth itself was not exempted from damage.

—Ngo The Vinh
Little Saigon, California
November 1986

ABBREVIATIONS

AID	Agency for International Development
ARVN	Army of the Republic of Vietnam
BBC	British Broadcasting Corporation
CIA	Central Intelligence Agency
CIDG	Civilian Irregular Defense Group
CTZ	Corps Tactical Zone
FULRO	Front Unifié de Lutte des Races Opprimées
FLC	Front pour la Libération de Cham
FLKK	Front pour la Libération de Khmer Krom
FLM	Front pour la Libération des Montagnards
GVN	Government of Vietnam
IVS	International Voluntary Service
LLDB	Lực Lượng Đặc Biệt (ARVN Special Forces)
LST	Landing Ship Tank

MACV	US Military Assistance Command, Vietnam
Mike Force	Mobile Strike Force
MSS	Military Security Service
NVA	North Vietnamese Army
RF-PF	Regional Forces–Popular Forces
SFOB	Special Forces Operational Base
STOL	Short Take Off and Landing
USAID	U.S. Agency for International Development
USIS	U.S. Information Service
VC	Việt Cộng
VNTTX	Việt Nam Thông Tấn Xã
	(Vietnam News Agency)
VOA	Voice of America

VIETNAM &
Central Highlands

CHAPTER ONE

The press card issued by the Information Bureau of the GVN, government of Vietnam, proved of little value; I came to see this clearly while traveling around the Central Highlands. At a time when the Americans had moved beyond the advisory stage, everyone knew this was their war—a war that had developed and was dealt with in the interests of the United States. Without a MACV press card, it was difficult for one to get through doors. How could the Americans trust a piece of paper not issued by them? When anyone could be viewed as a suspected subversive, there was no reason for me to enjoy greater privilege. With the press being considered an enemy by the government and mistrusted by the people—thus receiving no financial or logistical support—I definitely found myself bogged down and quite in isolation when dealing with the difficulties of my job. A veteran journalist once observed that making a living in journalism in Vietnam would eventually see one forced to become a hack writer and likely a bitter soul. Being also a painter whose way of life was colored by fantasy, I had no great ability to engage with reality; as a result, I continued to maintain an attitude of idealistic optimism.

In less than a month, I had experienced numerous changes in both my career and the routine affairs of life. Great effort must have been required to persuade the editor-in-chief to allow me to become a roving reporter, rather than requiring me to continue a safe vigil in the press room designing and laying out the paper. Even though he had accepted me in this new role after fulfilling a series of assigned tasks, the editor still made some rather harsh comments on my work. He said my prose was full of imagery and color, but was not in proper journalistic style. In his opinion, my descriptions captured feelings more succinctly than they presented the objective facts of reality, the task required in journalism. This failing on my part was not surprising, he added, to anyone who knew I had previously been a painter. In spite of that judgment, he seemed to have found in me something he liked, for he still encouraged me. Somewhere along the line, he even repeated the conventional wisdom that what is truly difficult is to improve and enrich something that is poor and insignificant—and one cannot place too much hope in that; on the other hand, changing from a flowery style to normal stern prose requires only self-discipline and some effort. I took this comment to mean that I should realize I had been somewhat careless in my writing and it was now time for me to observe the required principles and cultivate a more serious attitude.

It may be worth noting that the editor was formerly a well-known Southern businessman. Moreover, he had spent almost forty years of his life engaged in journalism. He was a link between the generation of pioneer journalists and this younger generation of today. He had a zeal for the career, and for an already well-to-do Vietnamese it was feasible for him to indulge his passion. As a rich man, he valued academic diplomas. Of course, he was sharp enough to recognize a good newspaper arti-

cle on its own merits, but if, in addition, it had any connection
with high academic achievement, this would please him even
more. For example, a doctorate in medicine would have no bearing on skill in writing battlefield reports, but to him that was a
celebrated mark very worthy of attention. Regarding myself,
given that my painting career—or my being a "painter," to use a
more flattering term—was not considered equivalent to an academic diploma, my name was appended to my articles lamentably
unadorned.

Routinely, each morning, when the paper had been readied
for printing, I left the office and walked downstairs to chat with
the girl who was the secretary, or went to the entrance of the alley
and ordered a cup of thick coffee. I then sat talking with who-
ever was around, usually printing shop workers or typesetters.

Peace and quietude filled the remainder of the day. Moving
from the initial step of the dark spiral staircase up to my office,
the air seemed to condense coldly. Black typewriters lay dormant.
Tables and chairs had their proper places relative to each other.
Sometimes, the familiar was tinted with the strangeness that had
marked the first few days following my arrival. Had I been painting still, perhaps I could have portrayed those first impressions.
Away from a canvas, I could not avoid longing thoughts of it.

After a fire had destroyed most of my work, I completely
abandoned the easel. Even so, in a recent exhibition, I had participated by hanging four large paintings: those remaining, which
had been scattered among friends. That my name was included in
the exhibition catalog was no cause for objection. However, of
great surprise was the fact that during the initial day of the exhibition my paintings were the first sold—three out of the four displayed. The one titled "Black Cat on a Pink Carpet" was bought
by a woman named Như Nguyện (the name means "full satisfac-
tion"), and the other two by an American who I later learned was
a journalist named Davis.

My paintings were among those difficult to appreciate, and therefore hard to sell. They were highly priced to make up for the small number sold. Because of this fact, with the sale of three paintings, I earned enough to pay off some big debts and buy another small typewriter and a very good camera. I felt like a farmer blessed with a rich off-season harvest. With this windfall, I decided to give up painting and its truly tardy rewards.

Davis and I were in the highlands. The air was dusty and insufferably hot.

He turned to me, seemingly sensitive to the vexation I had experienced all morning at various agencies, saying, "Triet, I still want to have you collaborate with me. After all, being with a foreign paper will facilitate your receiving all the required documents and identification papers."

Because of the contract with my paper's office, at this point I could not answer him one way or the other. I looked at him and said jokingly, "Not counting foreign reporters, only those from the government news agency have that privilege. Surely a MACV press card represents senior status in the profession. And one can proudly show it off!"

Davis laughed at this truism, recognizing it as comic satire.

The jeep bounced on dirt clods scattered upon the asphalt road, sending up red clouds of dust. The floor of the jeep was covered with sandbags, rendering heavy and lumbering the movement of the vehicle. On the positive side, one would choose to go slow with the sandbags, rather than fast without them, so that in the event the jeep hit a mine, one would likely survive and at least not lose one's legs. Situated within a controlled area that every day saw American soldiers on patrol, the road was relatively secure. Even though there was no fear of attacks or ambushes by the enemy, several times a month our side could not avoid sustaining wounds from mines or by sniper fire. An American advisor had suggested that we take a helicopter, but given that none was available, we decided to borrow a jeep and travel overland.

"In Vietnam," observed Davis, "transportation is a very big hassle. At times, it takes many days to travel a mere twenty or thirty kilometers."

I laughed and said that that was even truer when the area of operations was in the highlands.

We were on the same road upon which the minister, Dr. Denman, had been shot in the shoulder while driving back to his mountainous village late one afternoon. Though badly hurt, he still tried to make it home, but after driving ten more kilometers he passed out from loss of so much blood. The communists saw white missionaries as thorns needing plucking, especially a minister like Dr. Denman.

"Davis, do you want to end up driving with one arm like the minister?" I asked.

"If I knew I was going home to America soon, perhaps I would be anxious, but I still have to live this war for a long while yet. All American soldiers upon first arrival in country are the same: courageous and reckless, knowing no fear. Yet, during the final days of their tours, just before the trip home, all those who have survived with body intact suddenly turn timid as rabbits, afraid of being killed by a grenade or plastic explosives, even once having safely reached Saigon."

I laughed and commented that this was perhaps not the case with the Green Berets, those in the Special Forces.

Davis agreed and told me they were in a class of their own. "They are a new type of soldier born under the Kennedy dynasty. Beyond their incomparable lethality, they are a stubborn and undisciplined lot. Many American generals still refuse to recognize them as legitimate members of the army, like the other combat arms."

It took us more than three hours to travel a distance of no more than forty kilometers. We began to approach a very large Rhadé village. The tribal group living here was relatively civilized. They were well known for their warlike inclination, and their livelihood depended mostly on hunting. Under the influence of the minister, a rather large number of Rhadé had converted to Christianity.

Soon, houses on stilts were observed half hidden among trees. A moment later, seeing an unfamiliar car, naked children rushed over and happily shouted their welcome. A group of men with coarse hair and sun-baked skin, machetes in hand and woven rattan backpacks slung over their shoulders, quickly sidestepped to the edge of the road. They broke into big smiles, indicating they were not shying away because of fear of modern machinery.

Passing the village communal house, we reached Dr. Denman's residence. His abode stood by itself near a Special Forces camp. Inside, the building exemplified the uniform world of white men, with all the conveniences rich Western society provided. The altar for worshiping Christ was brightly illuminated with electric lights. A radio, a refrigerator, and food items were seen—all originating from the United States. In a corner of the house was a jerry-built radio transmitter.

Davis introduced me to Dr. Denman. I had often heard of the minister's reputation, read his book reviews in major newspapers, and been told quite different legends about him. He was, in truth, a missionary, a linguist, an anthropology professor, and author of the well-known research book entitled *Ethnic Groups of Mainland Southeast Asia*. Reading this book, I had felt rather embarrassed as a Vietnamese who did not know as much about his own country as did the book's foreign author. It appeared curious that experts on Vietnam were usually foreign professors, French in the past and American at present.

The minister was exerting great influence. With the help of Dr. Denman, Special Forces had been able to build their first bases in isolated tribal localities. The communists had lost their hold on people in the areas where his influence was felt. Having lived in the highlands for many years, Denman was well liked by a great number of tribal people, largely because of the practical help he extended to them.

According to Davis, Dr. Denman recently, with the assistance of Special Forces, was able to build a hospital to further expand the scope of his activities. In addition to his fluency in Vietnamese, the minister was also well versed in a number of tribal languages. He was inclined more toward activities of social work and research than to the task of spreading the gospel, which task received great care from his efficient wife. The couple lived with their eight-year-old daughter, who was born in this mountainous region.

The minister poured hot, thick coffee into white porcelain cups. "Coffee grown here in the highlands has a special fragrant taste, and so does the tea," he said. "I believe the local coffee can match any of the best varieties found in Latin America."

He lifted his cup and enjoyed a small sip to prove his point, then turned his attention to me.

Denman expressed himself with broad hearty gestures. He stated his opinion about the lamentable quality of the Vietnamese press. Many of his observations would have been sound if placed in the context of the United States, with its elaborate communications infrastructure and liberal democracy. I, however, was waiting for him to discuss issues in another area.

He proceeded instead by asking me what I thought the reasons were behind the dismal condition of the local press. I answered halfheartedly, blaming it all on poor means of communication and on strictness of censorship. He then moved on and discussed the necessity of limiting freedom of the press in countries where communists are present, and supported his argument by mentioning his own experience in several Latin American countries.

As if sensing my impatience, Davis reminded the minister of the purpose of our visit. But Denman did not show any sign of haste. He coolly turned to another subject.

"This morning," he said, "I visited a Rhadé village about eight kilometers from here. While there, by chance, I witnessed a bargaining session between an American officer and the tribal chief. The Special Forces captain wanted to buy a few elephants to be used in transporting supplies to some newly established camps in the forest. They kept on haggling over the price for a long while, with no end in sight. The captain finally lost his temper and shouted: 'Why don't you want to help us wipe out the communists? After all, they are Vietnamese also, and you want to kill all Vietnamese, don't you?' The unexpected result was that the American captain got the number of elephants he needed at a dirt-cheap price."

Dr. Denman had related the episode without showing his stand regarding it. At this juncture, he began to elaborate on the heart of the matter.

"In my opinion," he commenced, "objectively speaking, there has been an age-old antagonism between the people living in the mountains, popularly known as Thuong, and the Vietnamese living on the plain, popularly referred to as Kinh— origins of the antagonism resulting from discrimination and contempt for the Thuong held by the Vietnamese Kinh. The Kinh-Thuong relationship is very bad due to the deplorable attitude of the Kinh toward tribal minorities, whom they scornfully call Mọi, savages. In actuality, highly educated Thuong do exist, but are not allowed to participate in the government.

"Highlanders do not enjoy any more rights when they become Vietnamese citizens. Sometimes, they are even thrown

on trucks like animals and brought down to town to welcome
VIPs who purportedly came to visit them. On such occasions,
they must sacrifice a buffalo during the oath-taking ritual and
engage in a foot-washing ceremony while wearing their
bracelets, in order to show their sincerity and fidelity to the
guests. When the show is over, they are herded back into the jungle to continue their life of poverty and hunger."

The minister said all this while sucking on the stem of his
pipe, sending up soft blue smoke. He had a leisurely way of
talking.

Knowing that he was an anthropologist, I asked him to speak
about racial factors in the present conflict.

Denman said, "History and legend tell us that the whole of
central Vietnam, including the highlands in the old times,
belonged to the Thuong people, whose capital was bordered by
the coast on the eastside, thus probably indicating the present city
of Nha Trang. The tribal elders reiterate that the land of their
ancestors spread to the rising sun. This territorial extent existed
until the last of their kings fell passionately in love with a
Vietnamese princess of the north, and married her. The princess
became involved in a plot that destroyed the king. Thereupon, the
Thuong people became desolate, having no one to lead them, and
were cruelly driven into the jungle by the Kinh, where until the
present they have led a miserable life."

The imaginative character of my mind was strongly stimu-
lated by such a tragic but romantic past of a people brought to
ruin by a king's passion for a woman. Vaguely, I half listened to
Davis, who asked Dr. Denman about the state of newly built hamlets for the Thuong.

Dr. Denman shook his head in a show of exasperation. "The
Thuong are mentally looked down upon and they suffer ruthless
economic exploitation. Most of them hate to be pulled into the
social environment of the Vietnamese. Having lived their lives

freely in the natural environment of mountains and forests, they are now forced to concentrate in villages and hamlets built by the government. Such resettlement is not only an unwelcome change in lifestyle, but their security is by no means guaranteed in those new constructions. Every night the communists stealthily come to threaten them and rob them of their food.

"But if they were to try to free themselves from both the government and the communist sides by escaping to the forest and building their own hamlets, they would become targets for the government air force to mercilessly drop bombs upon.

"In short, they have nothing left, likely not even the future survival of their ethnic integrity and identity."

This was a dark picture of Kinh versus Thuong presented by the minister.

After tapping the bowl of his pipe against a wooden tray, he pressed his lips together tightly, then exhaled clouds of blue smoke. He possessed the leisurely manner of the traditional East, which exhibits no hint of the hurriedness prevalent in modern city life. Contrary to the image of him I had drawn in my mind, he appeared gentle and guileless. I noticed that the shoulder wound had healed.

The minister continued his discourse in a confiding tone. "Since the time that the program for pacification of the highlands fell into the hands of Americans, many things have improved. Very much unlike the Vietnamese, the Thuong get along well with white Caucasian soldiers. They trust that these foreign military men will defend them. In fact, when talking with me, Thuong leaders express their belief that after demise of the French, the Americans can help them rebuild an autonomous highlands region. This is their own aspiration, and I have no comment to make.

"It's curious, however, that Vietnamese appear to be very sensitive to racial issues like the problems between blacks and whites in the United States, yet they themselves seem not to recognize a similar mark of shame right in their own nation, where there is no shortage of ugly oppressions. And in that vein, the Americans' help for the Thuong has been considered a violation of Vietnam's sovereignty or an interference with her internal affairs. I, myself, can't understand this."

In a meeting like this, I saw no benefit in starting a debate that would surely be conflicted. I merely wanted to suggest a topic in order to hear what Dr. Denman would have to say. Therefore, I brought up a newspaper article published in the United States, which pointed out in a critical tone that the American superpower was helping Vietnam combat communism, and that, this being the task, there was no legitimate reason that American firepower should at the same time support the tiny nation's desire to realize its silly dream of creating an empire to rule over ethnic minorities. Upon reading the article's interpretation of recent historical events, I tried to imagine the type of empire that could be built by the wretched poor forced—initially by President Ngo Dinh Diem—to leave their villages for the forest, where they must toil to turn every square foot of virgin forest into cultivated land. What kind of empire could this become?

I stated this thought to the minister, but his tone remained coldly sarcastic. "The matter at issue is not simply that raised in this article. An uprising of the poor and wretched has its own legitimacy."

I had to restrain myself from expressing an angry response. A warm cigarette helped restore my calmness.

"By the way," I stated, as though the thought had just come up unpremeditated, "with regard to the letter addressed to the American ambassador and the United Nations by Thuong leaders in 1964, it seems you were consulted by these leaders many times, Minister."

With the exception of a mere fleeting instant of surprise, the minister's facial expression betrayed no emotion. He asked what I already knew about the letter. I told him I had read it, but was not sure if I had been reading a copy of the original text or a manipulated version.

Dr. Denman hesitantly regarded me, threw Davis a glance, then resumed his indifferent tone of voice. "As I've just told you, the initiative was theirs. I had no ideas of my own to contribute. Moreover, I did not want to invite misunderstanding, a misunderstanding that would jeopardize my religious mission, which has been going very well for more than ten years. The communists have accused me of working as a spy for imperialist America under the cloak of a minister. This does not bother me, as everyone knows it is part of communist propaganda strategy and their smear campaigns. But, otherwise, I want to keep my good reputation.

"I declined many times, but the Thuong insisted on securing my help. The only thing I agreed to do was to translate the letter into English and French. After that, they themselves had it typed up. They made copies, which they sent to the ambassador, the secretary general of the United Nations, and a few others.

"Subsequently came the December '65 event, a very bloody general rebellion of the Thuong, which occurred simultaneously in all highland provinces, and which was initiated by FULRO— Le Front Unifié de Lutte des Races Opprimées, or United Struggle Front for the Oppressed Races—a movement demanding autonomy for the highlands. FULRO is composed of three groups: the FLM, Le Front pour la Libération des Montagnards; the FLKK, Le Front pour la Libération de Khmer Krom; and the FLC, Le Front pour la Libération de Cham. But I'm sure you know all that.

"Naturally I did not approve of the uprising," he continued, "and so I no longer have communication with them. Even so, I still am experiencing misunderstanding and the expression of much ill feeling from a number of Vietnamese – especially General Thuyet."

Apparently, the little I knew about this matter had served as an invisible string tying myself and the minister into a discussion. Looking at me in a confiding manner, he attempted to establish a trusting atmosphere. He offered to show me the letter if I wanted to see it, but he did not think it was the proper time to publish it in the press as an open letter. Doing so would not be fair play, he thought, to those who had trusted him, and who were still pursuing their struggle.

Denman stood up and walked toward the bookcase, which was flanked by paintings of exotic tribal women.

Davis was deep in an agreeable conversation with Mrs. Denman, the two of them accentuating their talk with hearty laughter.

From the bookcase, the minister resumed his discussion by informing me that because of the close surveillance by the Vietnamese government in 1964, representatives of the Thuong when arriving in Saigon had not been given access to the American Embassy, and that upon their desperate entreaty, he had introduced them to a colleague of his, a Professor Milton Ross who was then teaching at University of Hue. Apparently, the letter had subsequently been handed to the ambassador by the president of Michigan State University. I was surprised to learn of Professor Ross's involvement in this event.

Quite engrossed in his conversation with Mrs. Denman, Davis seemed to pay no attention to what Denman was revealing.

The minister returned and gave me a hardcover folder holding typewritten sheets of paper. I had not at all hoped to have in hand such valuable documents, and when an opportunity like this unexpectedly came along, I knew I had to mobilize my mind to register the content and retain as much as possible. I chose to read the

French version of the letter very quickly and attempted to mentally summarize the details. Long lines were laden with doleful complaints. It felt miserable knowing more clearly their nature.

I sensed my emotional responses were being duly noted. Looking up, I caught a very peculiar expression on Denman's face. His watchful eyes were full of questions. I read the documents through to the last line, each word a needle pricking into my brain.

The minister told me further that there had been a few meetings, and what seemed to be a promise of possible assistance by the embassy, within certain limits. The group of Thuong leaders were disappointed because the promised support was too little, far below what they had hoped. A number of them had begun to establish contact with the communists to psychologically blackmail the American government. Others broke away and withdrew into the jungle with enough weaponry to embark on a long-term struggle, with or without assistance from Washington.

"I am sure you can see what a difficult position the Americans find themselves in," said Denman.

I returned the letter to him after having assured myself that I had memorized enough to substantially record it with the typewriter that evening.

Davis and I stayed on through the afternoon, then had dinner with Dr. and Mrs. Denman. It was a holiday and Mrs. Denman treated us to different types of canned meat. We also drank alcohol—not the type of spirits held in a jar and drunk through a long tube by some tribal groups—but very strong whiskey. Everything was uncomplicated and the atmosphere warm.

I looked at the image in Gauguin's "Christ Jaune" (Yellow Christ), a reproduction of which hung on the wall, and suddenly noted that I had never before been moved like this when viewing paintings. Detached from the anger and ambitions of exhausting struggles, I was suddenly my sentimental self again. It seemed as if I had never seen myself more truly a painter than I did at this moment.

Even though near midnight I was a little drunk in retiring to the room I had been given, I was inspired as never before. I sat at my typewriter and managed to record an abridged version of the letter—about a third of the original—together with observations worthy of attention made during the evening's discussion with Dr. Denman.

CHAPTER TWO

Darkness approached. We found it difficult to negotiate the jungle path, even though the remaining distance was no more than the smoke of a few cigarettes. Thuong people have the habit of measuring a distance by units defined on the basis of the time taken to leisurely smoke a cigarette, one filled with the strong tobacco available locally. Deciding to take precaution against possible contingencies, the commanding officer ordered tents pitched and guards posted, with the intent of advancing toward the target village at dawn.

This was the third day of a military operation being conducted under the *Đồng Tiến*, "Progress Together" program, an operation designed to liberate and evacuate Thuong people from isolated areas of the mountains and move them down to the edge of National Highway 21, a modern roadway as good as any found in Europe or America. Known as the M'Drack track a hundred years ago, this highway was then but a trail frequented by Thuong persons who traveled to the lowlands for exchange of goods.

Along this same trail at the beginning of the nineteenth century, departing from the coastal town of Nha Trang, Dr. Alexandre Yersin had penetrated the highlands and identified a suitable location for a resort, which became the town of Dalat. Dr. Yersin was a French bacteriologist of Swiss origins, born in Aubonne, Switzerland, in 1863, who died in Nha Trang in 1943. In 1894 he discovered the plague bacillus, named *Yersinia pestis* in his honor. Later, French expeditionary troops, who followed in Dr. Yersin's footsteps and fought to conquer the highlands, encountered fierce and heroic resistance from the local ethnic minorities. In the end, only because of the missionary influence of Catholic priests were the French able to gain a foothold in the highlands. And much later, in a similar fashion, ministers like Dr. Denman had helped the Americans build the first Special Forces camps in this remote area.

"Among the tribal chiefs known for anti-French activities, the most accomplished was Y Knul, a Rhadé man," said Y Chon, the unit's aboriginal guide. "Even today, when his name is mentioned, our old folk still remember him and tell us about his glorious feats of arms, his extraordinary skills in elephant hunting, and especially his invincible physical prowess—all of which made the mountain peoples venerate him as their Lord."

Y Chon, a Thuong person with a primary school education, was formerly an interpreter and sergeant working for the American Special Forces. Besides French and English, he spoke Vietnamese fluently. According to Y Chon, the next day we would arrive at a mountainous village called Nueng, inhabited by a population of Djarai people. This ethnic group still kept the custom of filing their teeth and elongating their ears, which made them appear ferocious. But, in truth, they were a gentle people living a life of poverty that was, however, free of worries about the future. Once a year, in the tenth month, they would slash and burn an area in order to plant crops, after which they would enter the forest to search for honey and cinnamon bark, and materials to weave rattan baskets for barter. Because they did not use paper money and placed value on objects solely on the basis of concrete form and function, in their bartering with people of the lowlands, the Thuong often suffered losses, their naivete being taken advantage of. With regard to the communists, not only did the Thuong dislike them, they also feared them. There had been some communist cadres who adopted the custom of tooth filing and ear stretching, spoke tribal languages, and lived like Thuong people in Thuong villages, but the communists' hope of attracting these mountain peoples to their side failed, as the Thuong realized they were being lured with false promises that would lead them nowhere.

The commanding officer's summons, heard over the field radio, interrupted Y Chon's monologue. He departed, clearly in a hurry. It was evening and I was left alone struggling to identify suitable tree branches from which to hang a hammock. My anxiety and fear upon finding myself deeply immersed in the jungle abated in view of the soldiers braving danger and hardship with little complaint. Moreover, the ability and skill of the commanding officer was to me reassuring. A graduate from Dalat Military Academy, he was well trained in jungle warfare and ever ready for battle. Though still a company-grade officer, a first lieutenant, he had a good record and had earned many medals. His subordinates feared him, and admired him as well: besides his skill in combat, the lieutenant was also known to be a savvy and worldly young man who, when removed from the battlefield, did not shy away from the world of decadence that Saigon had to offer. He recited names of the girls dancing at the Bacara nightclub as easily as he read complex military maps.

When talking about the *Đồng Tiến* program to resettle Thuong people along the highway, the Lieutenant had this to say: "We Vietnamese are those who provoke hostility and resentment, while our American partners grant favors. These Americans are

so shrewd and so unscrupulous! Are you aware of that, Mr.
Reporter? Our assignment is to evict the people and burn their
villages. The Americans reserve for themselves the noble task of
afterwards supplying relief. The inevitable result is that the resettled people blame the government of South Vietnam for whatever goes wrong, while being eternally grateful to the American
Embassy. I'm sure you well know that when the time comes the
Americans will cut off aid and the whole program will collapse.
We had a similar catastrophe only a few years ago while working
with Thuong impressed into the Strategic Hamlets Program."

There was a brief pause. "*Risque contre risque*," he summa-
rized, using the French phrase. "We South Vietnamese are in the
least favorable position and have no alternatives. Between the
communists and America, we have chosen the least evil enemy,
without entertaining any illusion about it."

Given his views, I was not surprised when on the second day
of the operation I witnessed a clash between the lieutenant and
his counterpart, the American advisor, First Lieutenant Schmidt.

"You can advise us only as far as aid is concerned. When it
comes to local knowledge and experience on the battlefield, you
people have a lot to learn from us," the lieutenant retorted when
the U.S. advisor criticized in a vituperatory manner the way in
which the operation was being conducted. At the same time, of
course, the Vietnamese officer was keenly aware that his unit
could not do without an American advisor, a prerequisite to
secure aid, air support, and air transport.

On the fourth day, perhaps in part uncomfortable because of
the lack of cooperation from the lieutenant, and partly owing to
the extreme physical hardships of the company operation,
Lieutenant Schmidt left the unit under pretext of illness. The
advisor boarded an evacuation helicopter sent by the sector command post, and this act was an omen that difficulties awaited us
in the days to come.

When Y Chon returned, the moon was high in the black sky. Through gaps between leafy branches, the jungle moon stood in beauty both virginal and majestic. I thought of the characterless moon hanging over the big city, and of friends quietly living their lives there. Only a few days ago I had led my life among them, and now I was lost in deep jungle. Such a huge gap between these two instances of the present!

"Are you not asleep yet? Did you hear anything unusual?" Y Chon asked.

I did not understand his question. Nor was I aware of any sounds other than those familiar in the environs of mountain and forest: the monkey's howling, the owl's cry, the crackling rustle of an unidentified bird flapping its wings. A stream ran between us and the village on its other side. I could hear the musical echo of water falling from a cliff and the sound of a thrashing wind. During my few days of forest travel, I had seen no trace of ferocious animals. There had only been snakes. Battles, bombs, and bullets had driven away jungle beasts, whose numbers had thus been greatly reduced—even though, previously, the tribes living in this forest were noted for their hunting skills.

"No, I didn't hear a thing. But what is it, Y Chon?" I asked.

"It isn't far from here. But since you are up wind of it, obviously you haven't picked up the noises. The reconnaissance squad came back to report that the villagers have been lighting torches, beating drums and gongs furiously. This is a local signal of unwelcome and of a willingness to resist and stop outsiders from intruding. It's fortunate that we haven't crossed the stream. There appears no indication they will attack. But security is the issue for tonight. All must be alert. I hope nothing untoward happens before morning; otherwise, our mission will be all the more difficult to accomplish. Moreover, you know, I don't speak much of the Djarai language."

"Certainly there must be some people in the village who can speak French."

"I hope so. But the main thing is that we have to be patient. We must show good will and friendliness, even if they provoke us or attack. Bloodletting invites only more blood debt. I have spoken of this to the lieutenant."

He was referring to "the call of blood," a flowery phrase used by General Thuyet—the former Commander of II Corps Tactical Zone—in essays he wrote on the Central Highlands. It appears that mountains and jungle had colored the general's soul with a touch of poetry.

Y Chon stated that General Thuyet was a commander with an iron fist wrapped in velvet; all struggling Thuong fighters were discouraged when hearing his name. "The general took pains to study several Thuong languages," continued Y Chon, "even though he was very good in French and his staff had more than enough interpreters."

"But how could he have learned Djarai when there is no written script for it?"

Y Chon laughed at my question and told me it was not that the Djarai had no writing system, but that they had lost it through negligence. "Tradition has it that when Buddha came to the highlands to teach, he acquired a lot of followers, and Thuong people came to him to learn how to write. While other peoples wrote on large dry leaves, like those of the banana tree, the Thuong people killed a buffalo and used its skin to write upon. When returning home, the Thuong tribal chief did not keep the skin entrusted to him in a safe place. During the night, while he was in deep sleep, his dog, smelling flesh of the skin document, snatched it away and chewed it up. In that incident, the Thuong people lost their writing script."

This legend of a deep sleep being responsible for disappearance of a writing system echoed the story of loss of the native land because of its king's blind passion for a woman, leaving, until the present, the Thuong people desolate.

The day's accumulated tiredness dissolved, along with thoughts of exhausting struggles: thus, one lived in the moment among simple souls and the sweet intimidation of wilderness. The cooking fires of evening had been extinguished, but the burned firewood showed still the dying traces of flame under ashes. Insects sang their laments; a snake whistled; human footsteps tread dry leaves. From the base of a nearby tree emanated a folk song sung in the voice of the ancient capital of Hue, an extremely melancholic voice, one filled with an unseen soldier's longing. I thought of Như Nguyện. I thought of the Perfume River flowing through Hue. I thought of my life there in the days to come. Như Nguyện was a dissolute woman who could not mix with others, for between her and ordinary life there was always a dividing wall. Lonely I was when away from her, while simultaneously knowing the fierce closeness of our passion spelled a moribundity of happiness. Loneliness becomes intolerable when the body is abused for the purpose of sensual exploration, I thought. Như Nguyện was completely lost to me at those sweetly intimidating moments of ecstatic writhing.

"Can you hear anything now?" Y Chon asked me.

It seemed the wind had grown stronger and changed its direction. Moonlight shimmered the surface of leaves. I now heard rhythmic drumbeats and the gong's aural titillation in distant echo, music melting into fog, very wild, yet carrying no violent note. Probably, at this moment, Djarai warriors were dancing around a fire, beating their instruments in urge of fellow fighters to be in readiness for reception of strangers from across the stream.

"The halt of our movement," said Y Chon, "was meant to be a sign of friendliness which would make it possible for us to proceed unhindered tomorrow. It's best not to have any bloodshed, because if we clash with courageous Djarai, the damage to both sides will be great. They are all sharpshooters. Not only with the bow and arrow, but with guns of all kinds: from the older Czech AK to the contemporary American M-16."

He paused to roll a cigarette, then lit it. "The likes of me can never be counted by them as a warrior," said Y Chon in a tone of self-mocking, smiling broadly, "as I have full teeth, considered by them similar to the fangs of wild beasts. At the age of fourteen, I ought to have practiced tooth filing. They consider the custom an expression of valor and courage. It is a terrible mental torture for a weak-hearted person even to watch it. Within only a day of initiation, the boy himself has to use a stone file or the serrated edge of a jungle knife to file his own teeth almost all the way to the gums. He must burn medicinal herbs on the blade of his knife and spread the ashes on his wounds to stop the bleeding."

The horrible sensation I had felt upon reading Jack London's descriptions of the skinning of human beings had not made me shudder as much as I now did at thought of the painfully prolonged death of nerves violently rubbed during a tooth filing operation. Indeed, Y Chon's account turned my teeth numb and my blood cold. The practice, as I saw it, was not merely based on the concept of beauty held by Thuong people, which had no place for the whole teeth of animals; it also represented an insightful philosophy concerning physical pain. By taking nature's challenge and choosing pain, these Thuong placed themselves to a level higher than whole-toothed beasts—not unlike the elevation of the Buddhist priest traveling his path of self-mortification.

Y Chon suggested I go to sleep to restore my energy for tomorrow's daylong journey. After he left, I tucked myself within a cotton sleeping bag, thoroughly enjoying the cover's warmth against the biting chill of jungle night. Exhaustion threw me into a full sleep of dreams punctuated by drummed rhythms and gong shimmers resounding from a village high up and far away, across the stream.

Though morning beckoned, it was still darker than night under jungle canopy. The soldiers arose and prepared their breakfast. The moon had sunk deeply into a sea of milky fog. Drops of stinging water dripped from trees, numbing my cheeks. My sleeping bag was soaked, as if having been exposed to a heavy rain. Such a hard life these soldiers lead! They never have regular hours to eat and sleep. They consume dehydrated food and drink water from streams, gathering edible greens and wild bananas to pacify stomachs filled with hunger. All the same, they sing songs in a life huddled next to death! I marveled.

As in the past three days, this morning I sat and chewed a bag of sun-dried cooked rice softened in water. The sweet taste of each mouthful anointed with soy sauce was so incongruously delicious that I thought I could indulge myself in eating it forever. I looked on as several soldiers gobbled up a basket of herbs scavenged from the forest. Only five in the morning, we finished our meals and packed tarps, tents, and foodstuff. We awaited orders. The scouting squad was sent out first. The rest of us were to follow at 7:00 A.M., when dawn had fully broken.

"Why did the village signal protest last night?" I asked Y Chon. "Do you think there are communist Thuong among them?"

"If there are, it is a matter of no real consequence. The Thuong mostly choose to avoid a clash, as you can judge by the non-event last night. Their loud protest, in my opinion, was due to many reasons. Foremost in circumstances like this is fear of the communists taking revenge. Thuong people do not like communists. They are very afraid of the cruelty of the communists. The *Đồng Tiến* program will collapse if we can't make the Thuong believe that they will be completely protected by the government."

"Being courageous and well-seasoned in combat, why don't they fight to defend themselves? Why should they rely on protection from the government?"

"They well know that the flamethrower and all the other forms of modern weaponry can wantonly cut down their bodies and mercilessly assault their courage. They are not foolish. Their philosophy, above all else, is to survive."

Y Chon made me fully appreciate that the times of bow and arrow, of primitive bamboo spear and blowgun, of the plain coarse dark cotton shirt were gone. No longer was there safety to be found deep in the jungle. No longer could guerrilla warfare be waged with relative impunity. All had been transformed, had taken on new dimensions.

Though morning sun in the highlands is never brilliant, this dawn it warmed us enough and demanded that evening fog melt away. Yellow light fanned out streamer arcs behind trees, revealing echoes of last night's moon. Birdsong danced aural highlights banishing lazy remnants of evaporating haze, accentuating details, overcoming merely conventional beauty in our surround.

The company spread out forming three salients, each of which was to cross the stream separately and from a different location. I accompanied the commanding officer in the middle salient. It took more than two hours to travel less than two kilometers along the jungle path. The scouting squad radioed their report. There was no sign of incipient resistance from the villagers.

The only remaining task for the company was to explain the operation and ensure security so household goods could be removed from village dwellings and carried to a transshipment point, from which vehicles would transfer both people and their belongings to the designated area of resettlement at the edge of the national highway. Contrary to yesterday's pervading tense anticipation, today everything proceeded smoothly, easy beyond expectation. The soldiers helped with hauling possessions. In each and every house, standing homey on stilts, nothing of value was left behind, except the odd utensil or an old wicker backpack.

The village chief, who spoke good French, told us that once in awhile communists came to harass the villagers, but would flee upon hearing approach of government troops. He was friendly and expressed his acceptance of the government's decision to evacuate his people. Everything went well.

I captured with my camera many exquisite shots. Young barebreasted Djarai women had all the natural beauty of Greek statues; in their manner was no overt suggestion of lurid sensuality, as depicted in the paintings seen at Minister Denman's house. I gave a young man a cigarette lighter in exchange for his bamboo pan-pipe, since he refused to sell it for cash. I intended to give this to Davis as a gift.

A terrible scream suddenly pierced the air, a scream of excruciating pain followed by a series of resounding gunshots. The gunfire obviously came from soldiers who had been posted at the jungle's edge as guards. Then the whole visible forest area went into pandemonium with barks of redounding fire and shouted orders to assault. The soldiers in the village quickly dispersed into defensive positions, leaving behind myself and those Thuong villagers who did not quite register what was happening but nonetheless turned pale with fear. My reflexive responses were momentarily numbed, and I had become almost frozen. Quickly, I was reassured, however, by the confident actions of the soldiers and the intense firepower I heard tearing through the opaque wall of jungle.

Horribly, it was Y Chon who had sustained the wound. He was struck by a poisoned arrow that penetrated deep into his left eye socket. Screams of pain at the puncturing projectile did not hide an obvious effect of the poison: his writhing about convulsively on the ground. Medics rushed to his rescue. They, and even the company medical warrant officer, appeared at a loss as to what best to do. The arrow was extracted trailing a line of blood.

Its shaft was covered with a black resin turning dark violet. Schmidt had left us. Without that American advisor, it was virtually impossible to request a medical evacuation helicopter to transport the wounded man out of the area. As the strong poison was flowing in his veins, it seemed likely he would not make it overland to the transshipment point.

All gunfire ceased and a desolate silence echoed through the jungle. The soldiers who had gone into the forest returned in a group, pulling along the corpse of a Thuong man, a thatch quiver of poison arrows still slung over his back. The archaic sniper's face was unrecognizable, torn apart by the impact of spinning and twirling M16 slugs, which had smashed into his head. Perhaps to avoid responsibility for what had transpired, the village chief declared that the dead man was a communist. It was uncertain where the truth lay.

Y Chon, meanwhile, was treated with herbal medicine. The writhing had abated, and there appeared to be increased hope that he would survive. Were he so lucky, he nonetheless would end up having lost an eye.

It was by now midday, and the sun had grown intense. As though intoxicated with gun smoke, the soldiers became heavy-handed and short-tempered. They set fire to all the houses in presence of the village's bewildered, devastated residents. With red flames dancing high and hot, they drove people and animals away from their homes, away from their native soil.

After many hours clearing the way, a convoy transported the people of Nueng village from the transshipment point to the resettlement area near National Highway 21. Not far from this location was an American firebase armed with many of the giant 175-mm cannons. I met Minister Denman and his wife at the reception center of the resettlement area.

Images of the killing poisoned arrow and of the fierce destructive impact of twirling M16 bullets clung to my awareness. It seemed to me that all the tragedies and all the Darwinian processes of development of human civilization for thousands of years were symbolized by the corpse of the Thuong man being thrown into the fire that day.

CHAPTER THREE

Traveling around the highlands, I rarely encountered American civilian or military advisors who had anything good to say about their Vietnamese allies. A similar observation could be made regarding the distaste shown by the American press concerning difficulties of the Kinh-Thuong relationship in the highlands. Even the book, *The Green Berets*, which exploded like a bombshell in the literary market, and became a national bestseller in the United States, aside from the main theme celebrating heroism of American Special Forces soldiers, presents the reader with nothing more than a display of those same soldiers denigrating and debasing their Vietnamese counterparts, the ARVN Special Forces, accusing them of incompetence and corruption, ridiculing them as being allergic to combat action. Most especially, the work describes cruel and barbaric behavior that Kinh lowlanders are said to exhibit toward Thuong highlanders, and sympathizes with the latter, who are said to be ill-treated, bullied, and even murdered without pity by the Vietnamese.

"Books like that just simply can't suggest to the American public and world at large good images of the Vietnamese people pursuing their struggle," I commented disgustingly to Davis.

This was not really a proper time to think idly of public opinion in Europe or America. We were standing in one of the hottest and most important locations of the war. The sun of high noon poured its extreme heat down upon us, turning the face of Davis lobster red. Tiny drops of sweat hung like warts on his curly long eyelashes. The dry westerly wind blowing through our loose-fitting shirts burned our skin. Roofs of corrugated metal—in their hundreds—crowded together, like hastily erected fairground structures, about a hundred meters back from a bend in Highway 21, a road that looked like a glossy black belt pounded by the sun. These were pre-fabricated houses put up upon a fertile yet uncultivated land, adjacent to a main road, and blessed with many streams. Every corner of the resettlement camp showed signs of attentive care. Drawing benefit from previous similar experiences, those responsible made sure the settlement area was prepared with considerable goodwill and a great deal of hard work.

But who could have anticipated all unexpected disasters and catastrophes? Counted as one such was a possible epidemic originating from the recent death of a Thuong man. The first problem was to persuade the bereaved family not to keep the corpse in their home too long, and to bury it soon. The second was to try to immunize the resettled people before an epidemic could spread and many deaths ensue. An inoculation task force, equipped with adequate serum, was mobilized; but upon this group's arrival, the Thuong found ways to hide themselves. When caught and held down for immunization, they resisted, screaming in fear and crying hysterically. After but a single morning's effort, an air of terror and anxiety hung heavily over several hundred homes. Davis and I received immunizations by way of demonstration. Finally, an artful scheme of both enticement and enforcement was conceived and implemented, which saw more than a thousand persons injected. Though this carrot-and-stick tactic was somewhat offensive, it served the purpose. Davis, nonetheless, seemed troubled and ill at ease with the heavy-handedness of a few of the soldiers.

"For hundreds of years they've led their lives separate from the outside world. Wouldn't you think it should take them some length of time to adapt themselves to new circumstances and the requirements of modern medicine?" Davis queried, the rhetorical question by no means having been uttered under his breath. "The situation here is no different from that faced by the first wave of Jewish people returning to their homeland—one characterized by alienation, confrontation with the unfamiliar, and unavoidable conflict. I hope this settlement will come to serve as a kibbutz-based model for other resettlement camps, a place where Thuong people are educated so they can catch up with our times."

Here Davis idealistically suggested a kibbutz formula for a promised land in the highlands. In reply, I told him that this would be something to think about in time of peace.

"No," Davis immediately protested. "On the contrary, the kibbutz is exactly the right and efficient social form in time of war. I have the impression that the border SFOBs are but a poor imitation of it. You don't see that?"

"Actually, to me, the Special Forces operational bases are purely military camps built by Americans, those from whom aid is fundamentally no more than alms tossed condescendingly to the inferior. The term 'kibbutz' is meaningless if it doesn't imply the spirit of communal living characteristic of a kibbutz."

"Well then, tell me," he retorted, "on the basis of what sort of vision was this camp here organized for these refugees from communism?" He brusquely swung his right arm around, indicating those seen about us.

"The term you mistakenly use, 'refugee,' itself implies temporariness," I answered. "This resettlement camp is not intended to be temporary. In fact, it is an attempt to carry out excellent plans conceived many years ago. In the main, this old yet still fresh idea is to gather together ethnic minorities who live scattered amongst crooks and crannies of the mountains; set them up in Hdip Mrao villages modeled on large village complexes with easy transportation access; educate them and help them adjust to community living; convince them to change their agricultural methods and to have trust in modern techniques, rather than placing themselves at the mercy of spirits and having faith in ceremonial offerings. Besides a dearth of material supplies, in my opinion, the really difficult task faced by the government is psychological preparation of the highlanders. Take, for example, the rather small matter of making use of improved farming implements. The issue is not so much to make available enough tools for distribution to farmers, but to somehow persuade them to reap rice with sickles, instead of using their hands to pull grains off each and every rice ear, so as to avoid punishment by unseen deities."

Davis paid close attention to what I had to say and did not hesitate to pose questions in order to clarify details.

"To eliminate superstition is perhaps more difficult than to break an atom," I continued, playing on Einstein's idea. "You know, President Ngo Dinh Diem applied the same basic plan, hurriedly, without careful preparation, and encountered fierce resistance from the Thuong. Thus arose the movement for separatism and highland autonomy. What counts is psychological preparation, without which this plan cannot be successful."

I did not know how long Davis had been in the highlands, but it was clear that he was very knowledgeable about all the political complications connected with the Thuong struggle. He resumed his questioning. "Having obtained a guaranty document from the office of the prime minister, how is it the leaders of the Thuong separatist movement still demand another guarantee from the U.S. Embassy before they will turn up for negotiations?"

That was news to me. It appeared Davis had more information in some areas than I did. By inference, I was myself trying to find an explanation.

"Even further than their aspiration for autonomy, there was a time when the Thuong wanted to join the United States of America as one of her states," I said. "Their simplicity and naivete has been an enduring stimulus for political sorcerers who want to propel the highlands into yet further adventures. History shows that even the French—wise and clever as they were—in the end couldn't accomplish their self-serving design for the Thuong. Applying their divide-and-rule policy for almost a hundred years, the French sowed the seeds of division among North, Central, and South Vietnam, between Catholics and non-Catholics; between Kinh and Thuong. In the last case, they restricted movement and contact between Kinh and Thuong peoples, allowing no migration of lowlanders to the highlands, giving the Thuong the impression that the mountainous areas were their own separate territory. In spite of all that, the highlands area in Central Vietnam was never cut off from the nation of Vietnam, and there existed no such thing as an autonomous highland country. Nowadays, through their interactions with American Special Forces soldiers, for example, many doors are open for the Thuong to look to the outside world. Though they may have been temporarily drawn into a political whirlwind, reality will break their illusions. A proof of this is to be seen in the fact that a few leaders of the separatist movement have switched their allegiance."

After a short pause, I continued. "The issue we are looking at here is freedom from ignorance and misinformation for the Thuong, and that is possible only through education and improvement of their knowledge. This forgotten war in the highlands, like that transpiring in the lowlands, will, as a matter of course, gradually die away only if and when social reforms have been carried out to raise the standard of living for all."

It occurred to me that deep down, in my heart, I was not actually so optimistic. My anxiety was augmented when I thought about shortage of competent personnel, indifferent attitudes, and deterioration of hope among average people. Even the so-called new policies promoted by the leadership were, at most, no more than patching holes in an old broken water pipe. The thoughts offered by a few individuals I had met or had known of— Professor Ross at University of Hue; Tacelosky, a USAID official; and Dr. Denman—reminded me that the path leading to a happy horizon for the highlanders was sure to be "longer than raising a cup of rice wine to your lips," to use a Thuong expression, a long and arduous path entailing much blood and tears.

"In your opinion, what benefit can the Americans derive from acting in such a contradictory manner—supporting the separatist movement of the Thuong while dying side by side with their Vietnamese allies?"

Davis's question came out direct and was unexpected. I recalled vaguely that a Japanese journalist, Takashi Oka, had posed a similar question to me. I had also asked myself the same question, and seeking the answer to it was the reason for my continuous travels throughout the highlands. At the same time, I was conscious of the fact that being a reporter I was an insider, an insider with a profound concern for the fate of my homeland. Many times I had been forced to make a choice between simple, straightforward presentation of the data I had gathered and my personal evaluation of the possible effects of various presentations of that data. On this occasion, in reply to Davis's inquiry, I chose to skirt the issue and gave him a roundabout answer. Davis appeared not to understand what I was alluding to, but he smiled and did not pursue the question further.

We both walked swiftly toward the administration office where we expected that Major Y Ksor would come to pick us up.

The major, himself a Thuong person, served in II Corps Tactical Zone as a liaison officer to help with resettlement of ethnic minorities.

On the way, Davis asked me to accompany him to the dispensary. The immunization earlier received had given him a slight fever, while I felt only a throbbing pain in my arm. These physical symptoms could easily be translated by superstitious beliefs into fears that could cause more than a thousand people in the settlement to rise up without warning.

Earlier in the evening, a film had been shown to a crowd of approximately five hundred curious viewers from this new Hdip Mrao village settlement. Midway into it, suddenly all hell broke loose, sending the audience running helter-skelter. The scene of a big fire shown on the screen frightened them. The reaction was beyond anything Davis and I would have imagined. Having often interacted with highlanders and being proud of my knowledge and understanding of their customs and practices, I still found myself over and over again faced with new discoveries.

Davis asked me, for comparison, about the condition of highlanders in North Vietnam.

"The standard of living of the mountainous people in the north is relatively higher, thanks to easy communication and interaction with people of the plain," I replied. "But that doesn't mean they experience no ethnic conflict. As for the southern highlanders, though it has been more than one hundred years since Dr. Yersin set foot in this highlands region, the results of the French *mission civilisatrice* is what you have just witnessed. Things remain the same here like secular trees forever dormant on the hills and in mountainous villages. It's rather sad that toward the end of the twentieth century, in a nation priding itself on four thousand years of civilization, there should exist a few dozen ethnic groups who have yet to depart from the Stone Age."

"I read some materials from the University of Stockholm, in which a Vietnamese anthropologist, whose name I don't remember, expresses his opposition to the idea of assimilation of ethnic minorities into the Vietnamese mainstream. He only concedes to what he calls 'cultural adjustment,' by which I suppose he means a soft form of acculturation."

I thought I knew who Davis was talking about. The man was at present a professor in the Faculty of Letters at the University of Saigon. He possessed profound knowledge of the Thuong people. The professor nurtured the dream of following in the footsteps of personalities like Rondo who set up agencies for the protection of aborigines in Brazil. As a reporter habitually looking at the ethnic issue from a political and social point of view, I did not share his concern.

I laughed and said to Davis, "The object of study of anthropology is human beings. Just like a painter, an anthropologist is excited with unusual and rare subjects. As such, he feels regret over the mixing of races and change in old customs and practices. Let's leave the artist and the anthropologist alone with their exaltation over their subjects. It's not necessary to set up associations for the protection of highlanders here in Vietnam, as we don't have people out here searching for and killing these counterparts of the American Indians as though they were game animals. The crucial and urgent matter of concern is to eliminate the gap between Kinh and Thuong through a progressive and civilized large-scale program. For example, in newly built mountainous villages we may encourage Thuong people to stop wearing loincloths and to pay attention to hygiene, without violating the beautiful cultural practices which they cherish. We can't possibly consider backwardness as being culture, and we should not, in a distorted way, see each tribesman as an antique item to research and preserve."

Needless to say, I was not in agreement with this anthropologist, whom I had never met and who was not present. Perhaps his passive intellectual attitude was too much of a contrast with the image I had formed of the aggressive and practical minister, Dr. Denman. In connection with this, it was in bitter irony that I heard Davis's responding statement, wherein he proclaimed that to know and understand ethnic issues in Vietnam, there was no better way than to read what foreign authors had to say. I myself had more than once experienced such a discouraging discovery, and therefore had no reason to regret having missed the opportunity to spend long years at a Vietnamese university. Our civilization, of allegedly four thousand years' duration, appeared completely empty to me. In any event, on my next return to Saigon, I intended to look up this anthropology professor. My career in journalism had often enough placed unwelcome encounters in my path.

"You well know that in a politically confusing situation like Vietnam at present," I concluded, "anthropological research is being used as no more and no less than a means to effect political divisions."

The evening air became mild and pleasant. The sky lowered itself to the earth. From the nearby American firebase, cannon rounds discharged, swooshing toward deep jungle, their explosive echo shaking hills and mountains, agitating even moon and stars. The victims might be communists in hiding, a group of Thuong yet to be evacuated, even hapless animals that had unknowingly ventured into a free-fire zone. Bullets and fire, even when not issued by the enemy, terrified the Thuong.

Then silence prevailed, silence sudden as the deadly explosions preceding it, a silence triggering emotions neither joyful nor sad. Again, in moments like this, my thoughts turned to Như Nguyện, and I missed her sorely. Had she been here beside me in place of Davis, I would have been very pleased to accept the invitation to dinner extended us by several village chiefs. Như Nguyện would learn to drink local rice wine through a bamboo tube. I would remind her to accept the tube with her right hand when it was passed to her, as I remembered she had the habit of using her left, which was taboo to Thuong people. They considered use of the left hand a gesture of provocation and contempt. Her ignorance would unknowingly dampen the friendly relations between hosts and guests. But I also knew only too well that Như Nguyện would in no way choose to spend her time with me here. To maintain our love relationship, either she or I would have to abandon our chosen way of life. As for that, I had made a decision. I would leave behind my job with the newspaper and move to the city of Hue.

Major Y Ksor sent someone to fetch us. We were to appear at the village communal house. During dinner, Davis declared that this was the first time he had enjoyed game meat so deliciously roasted. Though we had difficulty communicating across the language barrier, both hosts and guests treated one another with utmost respect and cordiality. A few Thuong, who had recently performed the required tooth filing, could not partake of their meals with ease, as it hurt to chew. Normally, they would have eaten congee or a type of millet cooked in water until very soft. When indigenous rice wine was offered, Davis was the first to quit drinking, probably because he was not used to the taste, which he claimed to be too sour and bitter. Sitting beside a jar into which the host village chief continually added water, I kept up with Y Ksor and drank all the way to round three of the ritual. Watered-down, still sweet and pungent, the spirits lost little taste. In this relaxing atmosphere, all sorrow and anxiety stepped out the door, and I came to understand why Thuong people choose hunger three to five months a year, in order to save enough rice to produce spirits for their months-long spring celebration.

CHAPTER FOUR

A telegram announced that Như Nguyện was awaiting me in Dalat. As might have been expected, she was in the same Rose Street mansion we had occupied several times in the past—which looked like a palace. Unfortunately, for the next few days, I would still be busy with an unfinished task. Indeed, I did not have much time to spare, as I had to cover the news that the lieutenant colonel who was chief of II Corps Tactical Zone Psychological Warfare Bureau was about to be transferred by General Tri to another post. General Tri had replaced General Thuyet.

On my way to II Corps Headquarters for my appointment with the lieutenant colonel, I stopped by the local post office—small as a box—where I sent Như Nguyện a wire promising to meet her in two days. Knowing her as I did, there was no entertaining the thought she would wait for me in that resort city; she would go back to Saigon this very afternoon. If only she had been by my side now; how happy a moment that would have been! But she would not be sharing my longing, and perhaps would never even consider it.

Suddenly I had no desire to go back this evening to my poor, depressing room in the hotel, spending time there alone, laboring at the typewriter so as to have an article ready for dispatch on the first aircraft bound for Saigon in the morning. Perhaps this article would turn out to be no more than a collection of reflections on things seen and heard during the days I personally observed the operation to resettle our ethnic minority fellow countrymen.

Having tossed aside a paintbrush to pick up a writing pen, to use the Vietnamese idiomatic expression, I became by habit weary of criticism—even constructive criticism. This was not because of the fear that such criticism would land me in difficult straits vis-à-vis government officials or military officers, especially so in regards to General Tri. Rather, my concern had to do with the degree of usefulness of my writing efforts. I did not want to attempt what the Rhadé highlanders described as trying to force light buoyant dried bamboo stalks to stay below the water's surface. Impossible task. But in a dark situation with gloomy prospects, hope had to be rekindled—even if there would come but a few tiny sparks of light.

"This is the bottom. I can't fall any further than this," said the colonel when I entered his office. "Wherever I am to be transferred, it can't be worse than where I have been. If I was to be sent to a combat unit, that would be all the better: more suitable to my real ability and skills."

This was the first time preceding his expected departure that the colonel expressed discontent. He had been an excellent officer during President Diem's time, serving as Ben Tre province chief. After the fall of Diem in the so-called revolution of 1963, as a punitive measure, the new government exiled him to the Central Highlands. He was a true public servant who performed his services wholeheartedly and with diligence, even in his then and present less-favored positions. I also learned that during the

first years under President Diem's regime, when the present lieutenant colonel had already become a major, General Tri was then
but a lower-ranking company-grade officer, and that the colonel
currently was the individual who had held his present rank the
longest without promotion.

Giving me a folder in hard cover, the colonel asked that I
grant him the special favor, if at all possible, of not releasing in
my newspaper any information from it. He explained that what I
had in hand was a classified dossier that was to General Tri a
bone caught in the throat: he could neither swallow nor remove
it. Even as I wondered why he had decided to give me this confidential information, he revealed that when we had first met he
had felt that he could trust me, and he still believed in this initial
intuition. Nonetheless, he exhibited some anxiety and urged me
to be cautious.

"Be on your guard," the colonel said. "General Tri doesn't
much like the press. Your presence here is a thorn many people
would like to pluck. Difficulties may arise for you at any time. But
as long as I am here, within the limits of my authority I will try to
help you. I revere discipline and respect principle, but I also know
where their limits lie, and where exceptions should be made."

He laughed uttering this, but could not hide the sad note in
his voice.

I opened the folder and was faced with files upon which the
words "secret" and "top secret" were stamped in red. Once again,
I had to make the most of the capacity of my brain to quickly register information, as I did not have time to take notes. These were
letters and documents captured from a separatist camp, most of
them written in French, including leaflets addressed to the
Thuong people calling upon them to rise up and fight for their
autonomy. Ironically, 99 percent of the highlanders were illiter-
ate. All the tragic and heroic history of the highlands seemed to

be symbolized by the legendary or exemplary life story of a Thuong man who had been lured by communist 1954-stay-behinds to fight on their side in the name of Uncle Ho. Later on, realizing that he was being duped and taken advantage of, the man left the communist camp and fought alongside the Americans. The Thuong were pulled hither and thither by all sides in the conflict—the nationalists, the communists, and the Americans—even though motivations in the war had virtually no connection with the lives of Thuong in their mountainous home-land. As I read along, words in their rows brought to my mind's eye details of a bloody page in history. And, commonly, blood calls for more blood, as had been proven by the merciless han-dling of the Thuong separatists by General Thuyet when he was in command of the highlands.

When informed that General Tri was about to arrive, I closed the folder and returned it to the colonel, not without securing his promise that I would be allowed to come back for a further read-ing. I made an immediate departure.

Because it was still too early for the rendezvous I had arranged with Davis, I walked downtown and bought a few news-papers. All the papers arrived here a day later than the date of issue. Among the familiar pages with their familiar columns, I found an article by Prof. Hoang Thai Trung, which criticized the book entitled *The Green Berets* in his typically vehement style of writing. Besides his usual sharp and profound observations, in this article his tone was also touched with vexation and bitterness. This was the first time I had seen him lose his normally calm man-ner and allow himself to embark upon arguments laden with emo-tion. That element of fire sustaining an intellectual's youthfulness! I thought of Trung. I thought of Hue. I thought of the coming days' uncertainty when I would live with Như Nguyện in that

ancient city. A special circumstance had witnessed my first introduction to Mr. Trung, a circumstance held vividly in memory.

After the seemingly successful exhibition in which I had participated with four of my paintings, a gathering of noted writers
and artists had been organized upon the initiative of the foreign
minister—of all people. After the revolution of 1963, which
marked the end of President Ngo Dinh Diem's regime, and along
with the escalation of the American war, South Vietnam experienced a time of upheavals with one coup d'état following another. Successive governments had no clear-cut strategy, no explicit,
well-formulated policies. Everyone felt he had to do something
worthy of the revolutionary spirit. The result was that various
ministries took upon themselves the task of designing their own
agenda, as befitted their new ideas, within or without their areas
of expertise and operation. Thus, the Ministry of Culture and
Education came up with an idea about foreign relations, an idea
aimed at gaining for itself some diplomatic merit; thereupon, it
busied itself with organizing groups of students to send to
America and Europe. It was expected that these students would
neutralize the antiwar movement raging on university campuses,
a movement marked with sit-ins and teach-ins, and defend the
unconditional involvement of the U.S. army in the war.
Conversely, the Ministry of Foreign Affairs turned to internal
affairs—sponsoring, for instance, meetings of writers and
artists—and, by introducing its large-scale plan for cultural openness, embarked on an area of activities normally undertaken by
the Ministry of Culture and Education.

At the gathering organized by the foreign minister, aside
from a few painters who were my close friends, I had recognized
a number of dominant figures in the arts and literature. Among
them was a typical anticommunist writer of the 1940s generation; a young writer of the lost or alienated generation, in whose

works the first-person protagonist was usually a female; and a well-known playwright who had, strangely, as I knew, not written any play.

I particularly noticed the presence of the literary critic Hoang Thai Trung. Very young, he was a journalist and university professor who constantly tried to heighten people's awareness of the dark and obscure meanings of the current war. His writings had a great impact on the young and were considered to represent the fruit of a socially concerned intellect. By virtue of this point of view, he was labeled a communist by many; but since he was a Catholic, the label had a hard time sticking, as it was believed Catholic people could never live in peace with communists. This premise did not prove quite correct, for it was later learned that he left the government camp and joined the opposite side.

The presence of this controversial personality made the foreign minister uneasy. Both had been journalists, as indeed, at the time of the meeting, Trung still was. Various conflicts had transpired between the two, made public in several battles of words, as a result of which Mr. Trung was classified by the authorities and the Americans as a dangerous leftist element.

As for the foreign minister, until the time of this gathering of writers and artists, I had heard his name without knowing what he looked like. Coming from a family of well-known Confucian scholars did not protect him from the widespread public opinion that he was a member of the president's cabinet heavily involved with the Americans. At a time when rumors occurred in abundance, people were inclined to suspect everything they heard was false, even when the rumor was, in truth, an actual accusation.

I knew that the minister was originally the editor-in-chief of one of the two English-language newspapers in Vietnam, that he openly exhibited a pro-American attitude, and that he defended without reservation the presence of the American army in Southeast Asia. Concurrently, he also displayed an ardent anti-communist position, and no one could deny that fact, a fact that itself was the necessary, if not sufficient, reason that he was trusted with important work by the Americans. While being a Vietnamese diplomat, he was a loyal spokesman for the policy being pursued by the Americans.

On the other hand, according to the judgment of those close to him, he was the veritable image of a national spirit, a national spirit that, unfortunately, was fading to a lamentable degree. On his initiative, the gathering of writers and artists was supposed to be an occasion to plan introduction of Vietnamese cultural achievements to foreign countries, something that North Vietnam had long been doing. This was a great plan on the part of the foreign minister, but in the main the discussion turned out to be poor, leading to no practical result—not to mention the fact that the guidelines advocated by the foreign minister were based on an extremely elementary concept of art. Nor was there any pleasure to be taken from dwelling on the memory of the obsequious flattery and groveling entreaty committed by those who called themselves writers and artists.

Also at this same gathering I met Như Nguyện, the woman who had bought one of my paintings. As the cultural attaché at the Vietnamese Embassy in Tokyo, she was back in Saigon for some sort of consultation with the foreign ministry and was asked to come along to the meeting. At that point, I had not imagined there would be connections between her destiny and mine. In truth, until then, I had been unable to gain real knowledge of, and had received little information about, this woman—outside of the fact that her presence was characterized by a wild lifestyle that earned her a bad reputation.

To me, Như Nguyện had the marvelous appeal of a skylark, a type of bird that flies very high and sings its song beautifully. Once, from Tokyo, she wrote me a long letter that discussed nothing specific, but revealed she was experiencing emotional turmoil. She compared herself to a little bird trying to flee from snow, a very lonely bird. She wished I had kept her confined to one place, just as I had kept the black cat confined to the warmth of the pink carpet in my painting. I missed her, and felt that, if I ever returned to painting, that return would have much to do with such intimate personal feelings.

When I showed up at our appointed place, Davis was waiting anxiously for me. Major Y Ksor had urgently sent someone to bring us back to the village communal house. He felt growing hostility in the atmosphere, the tension reaching its peak when spiritual and religious issues entered the picture. The whole Hdip Mrao village, which yesterday had been peaceful, suddenly became tumultuous, as if ready for an uprising.

"Kdi rai Cam, ram Yuăn," Y Ksor exclaimed. All had been destroyed, just like in the aftermath of the battle between the people of Champa and the Vietnamese.

Indeed, all the hard work that had been put into preparation of the settlement area seemed to have been wasted effort. More than a thousand resettled highlanders unanimously stood up, demanding their return to the deep jungle. Though frightened, they determinedly resisted those soldiers who tried to restrain them.

"Why?" I asked Major Y Ksor. "Is it because they are dissatisfied with not receiving enough supplies?"

"No, that's not it at all," the major answered. "Since this is meant to be the model demonstration project of the resettlement program, one can say that supplies are most abundant. I think the lieutenant is the cause. He is still young and aggressive and, being a Kinh person, cannot understand them."

Hearing himself discussed, the lieutenant protested Y Ksor's judgment. He firmly argued that the person who had initiated the ongoing crisis was a Thuong communist infiltrator who had used sorcery of some sort to incite people to rise up.

Even in circumstances as difficult and confusing as this, Major Y Ksor maintained a remarkably cool demeanor. He calmly said to the first lieutenant: "I know of and admire you for your experience in jungle warfare. However, with regard to knowledge and understanding of Thuong people, with all their superstitious customs and practices, I don't think you are my equal, for the simple reason that I am a Thuong person myself. It's not that I want to place the blame solely on your shoulders, but it was precisely the arrest and torture of their shaman that caused this tense situation. What I regret most, given that our fellow countrymen are still very superstitious, is that we did not first of all try to persuade and convince their shaman."

As it turned out, in their accustomed life of shifting agriculture, whenever they arrived at a new location, the Thuong villagers always had their shaman conduct a prayer ceremony to ask the land deity they called *Thần Nhang* for permission to stay. If there was already some sign that permission was denied, but they persisted in staying, they believe that the deity would punish them by causing diseases and deaths. And in the present situation, they were trying to get far from a piece of land they believed full of ghosts, devils, and death—as interpreted by their shaman when the strange inoculations gave them throbbing arm pain, and when a Thuong man chose to die on the day of their arrival.

Y Ksor turned to me and explained. "Did you hear that, Mr. Reporter? No matter how fully equipped we are with material supplies, we can easily fail if we neglect to prepare their mental state in regards to the evacuation."

The lieutenant, a reasonable man, asked Major Y Ksor what he and his soldiers could do in the present circumstance. Having apparently firmly grasped the situation, the major immediately suggested a possible solution. "Thuong people are by nature very gentle, but they can turn violent when in fear. To forcefully keep them longer in this resettlement area only serves to increase that fear. You should let them go, continue to keep an eye on them, and help them. I don't think they will go deep into the jungle, there to be accidentally shot or to again face communist guerillas whom they hate. This piece of land perhaps cannot be used again for the same purpose; we can put it to some other use. We will evacuate the villagers to a place a few kilometers from here, also near the highway, and I will try to persuade their shaman to obtain the local deity's acceptance."

Many difficult issues remained for Y Ksor to resolve, including mollification of the innocent shaman who had been beaten until his face was swollen. He also expressed his anxiety about the presence of several foreign reporters. Quite possibly these foreign members of the press would explain the conflict as a result of contempt and ill treatment meted out to the Thuong, who were forced into what Western newspapers have called concentration camps, where they are abused and even killed. Following from that, the argument would go, the highlanders had to risk their lives to return to the deep jungle. Seen in this light, perhaps Minister Denman was wise enough to have earlier withdrawn himself from the scene, so as to avoid association with such misconceptions.

Throughout the whole evening, sitting beside a jar of rice wine, Y Ksor, like a talented diplomat, managed to pacify the shaman and even the village chiefs with his apologies and promises for continued help to them. He also promised to start building a new Hdip Mrao village on a benign plot of land where *Thần Nhang* would allow them to stay.

The air seemed more peaceful, the tension under control, but that did not help cancel determination of the Thuong to leave. In the morning, the lieutenant ordered the barricades removed. Long lines, composed of people holding children and pulling animals, formed and shuffled eastward into green jungle, moved toward blue mountains in the distance. None had any notion of a specific location where they were heading. When the last group had departed, leaving behind corrugated tin roofs shimmering under the sun, Y Ksor looked around at the new village, empty of inhabitants like a deserted market. Tears welled in his eyes, and he clenched his teeth to suppress a sob.

CHAPTER FIVE

As the lieutenant colonel commanding the Psychological Warfare Bureau in II Corps liked to say, General Tri got along famously with the Americans because he advocated harmonious coexistence and collaboration. General Tri was the replacement for General Thuyet, who had been transferred to I Corps Tactical Zone. In a war that had been Americanized, General Tri well knew that he would not have much difficulty in asking the Americans for things in return for his ready compliance to their demands. This approach made him very different from General Thuyet.

The matter of the Thuong people, for example, caused General Thuyet so much trouble because he had insisted on dealing with it all by himself. Now that the whole Thuong problem was entrusted to the Americans, everything seemed to be going smoothly for General Tri. But this could be a deceptive smoothness, one that might backfire beyond salvage at some point.

The *Đồng Tiến* program was proceeding tentatively, with plenty of unforeseen difficulties. The ARVN could only conduct operations into deep jungle and evacuate their Thuong fellow countrymen to the edge of Highway 21. The resettlement strategy, with its required logistical support, heavily depended on the Americans' ability to dispatch aid. This arrangement rendered the Vietnamese partners of the Americans most vulnerable to sabotage.

The trouble in the new Hdip Mrao village had just been resolved satisfactorily by Major Y Ksor when General Tri had had to confront another problem. It began with the arrival the day before of a Thuong man who had courageously escaped a siege and traveled many kilometers through thick jungle to seek help from the ARVN. The heart of the situation was the fact that more than six hundred Thuong people, located in the Dakto Tri-Border Area and coerced by the Viet Cong to do forced labor, were in the next three days to be driven across the border and out of South Vietnam.

Because it was beyond his authority to decide on a course of action, Y Ksor took the man to General Tri. This Thuong man spoke Vietnamese with difficulty, and chose clumsy words—words that an ungenerous person might consider indicated impoliteness toward the general. Seeing that the general appeared irritated, Y Ksor immediately tried asking the man a question in French, to which he answered in fluent French. The general allowed the Thuong to continue in this foreign language more familiar to him.

When asked about his people's feeling toward the communists, the man replied: "Simply mentioning the Viet Cong is enough to scare us to death. We villagers call them 'bats.' As for violence, we think of them as ferocious tigers. They force us to work for them, transporting bullets for them. They also tax us: rob us of rice and domestic animals. If we ever thought of leaving, they would threaten to kill the whole village. None of us are allowed to go away from the area for more than a few kilometers."

General Tri cross-examined the man. "If the situation is as tight and dangerous as you say, how did you manage to bring yourself here? Or did the communists send you here to tell us such a story?"

The general's suspicion sent the man into a panic. Only the calm expressions on everyone else's faces reassured him.

"Please, General," the man stammered. "You know well we are very miserable. If I lied to you, my wife and children would be dead. We villagers can only pray for the government's protection, so we won't be forced to slave for the communists on the other side of the border."

Ignoring the Thuong's verbal supplication, the general, in a characteristic Vietnamese gesture, jerked up his chin in the direction of Y Ksor. "Well, Major," he queried, "how far can you trust the words of this man?"

Not quick to make an answer, Y Ksor turned and addressed a string of words to the Thuong in a tribal language. The man quickly uttered his answer. Staccato sounds joined one another in several cycles of questions and answers. No one witnessing the exchange understood what was being said.

If General Thuyet had been present, thought General Tri, he would have spoken directly with the Thuong in his own tribal language.

Finally, Y Ksor asked the man to wait outside, then turned to the general. "General," he said, his voice determined and firm, "upon the honor of my rank, I guarantee that what he has told us is true. One thing that no one can deny is the hatred which we Thuong people have toward the communists. This explains why, after years living among us, even after adopting our custom of tooth filing to prove their allegiance, the communist infiltrators have not been able to gain our loyalty and trust. We are well informed now, and we know who truly wants to help us and who is out to exploit and take advantage of us. I think this is a good opportunity to show that the government truly cares and wants to extend help to the Thuong people. And I am sure such a gesture will not be forgotten by them."

Full of emotion, Y Ksor talked without pause.

Impatient, General Tri interrupted him and, looking toward the rest of the staff present, said, "I know all that. But how do we help them?"

Not happy with the interruption, Y Ksor continued as soon as the general had finished posing the question. "Please, General. Please consider the time factor. The man told me that only two more days are left before the VC will drive all these six hundred people to the other side of the border. Actually, an earlier date had been given, but was postponed when the villagers said they had to complete the harvest and pointed out that the VC are in need of rice, too. So the issue is not whether the government has the goodwill to help the villagers, but how the government can save them from oppression and slavery before it's too late. Moreover, the notorious movement for highland autonomy waits for any sign of impotence on our part, so as to exploit the situation and agitate people for subversive action."

Turning to his operations officer, the general asked for a summary of the situation.

Walking to a map holding a stick, the officer circled an area with rapidly inscribed arcs of the stick's point. "The village we are talking about is located here in the middle of Vùng Tam Biên, the 'Tri-Border Area'."

He repeatedly tapped the map.

"Laos is to the north; Cambodia, to the south; Vietnam, to the east. The southernmost edge of the area is at the Cambodian border where the Ho Chi Minh trail passes through it. This is the tail end of a hidden, deep valley, quite isolated from its surroundings."

The point of the stick swept the map over the valley's location.

"Previously, it was relatively secure, thanks to a Special Forces camp nestled near its mouth. After the failed FULRO rebellion of September 1964, when most of the Thuong soldiers in the valley fled to Cambodia along with their weapons, the American advisors, facing many difficulties, also removed themselves from the area. As a result, the valley became a contested location, and has periodically been used as a rear-services center for VC units.

"This valley is less than a hundred kilometers from us. It is surrounded by jungle scattered with guerrilla units, mines, and booby traps. Though they can't gather an adequate fighting force to engage in large battles, the enemy would still cause us severe damage in numerous other ways, if we were to go deep into their territory.

"The Vietnamese Brown Berets surely could send in small ranger units, but they could only conduct surveillance and act as forward observers. In short, the issue we must face is twofold: First, to send in a force large and powerful enough to stay engaged for a minimum of two days in an operation to disrupt the VC's effort to drive the villagers across the border; and second, to secure means of transportation sufficient to evacuate more than six hundred people, together with their possessions. Both could be carried out with the help of the American's airlift capacities."

Upon mention of a solution that would require American involvement, General Tri seemed to grow quite weary. The truth was that help would not come without some sort of shameful bargain. No doubt the general was thinking of the cold face of Tacelosky, the USAID advisor. A retired lieutenant colonel who had earlier served with Special Forces, the man was now a high-ranking CIA officer using USAID as his cover. Tacelosky's authority extended to embrace the role of liaising with MACV concerning virtually any area he felt fell within his purview.

In a clear, resonant voice, the chief of staff cut in and presented details of the projected operation, then concluded, saying, "To sum up, what we will need is fifty helicopter flights to transport the soldiers and to evacuate the people. Only the base at An Khe is able to help us with this. The matter will depend on your direct intervention, General."

The chief of the Psychological Warfare Bureau counseled the general on how to proceed. "We should try to directly contact General Hunting at An Khe and ask him to help us, without going through Tacelosky. Whatever goes through the man gives him a chance to blackmail us in one way or another, especially given that he wants to prove the impotence of the government of Vietnam to help and protect the Thuong people."

This astute suggestion met with General Tri's complete agreement.

Having had the Thuong man brought back into the room, the general publicly announced his promise to help, but also informed the man of possible adversities. The radio communications unit was ordered to contact An Khe immediately.

Fortunately, General Hunting had just returned to the base from Saigon. A graduate of West Point, he was a courteous and highly principled officer. He had easily established many friendly relationships with Vietnamese officers. General Hunting expressed his readiness to help General Tri, and agreed in principle to the latter's plan of operation. But precisely because of the matter of principle General Hunting had to consult Tacelosky.

Though he was not fond of this American CIA officer who posed as a USAID official, General Tri was obliged to invite him to his private residence for lunch. The general had reason to be anxious about difficulties that would transpire during their meeting. In order to avoid embarrassment and a loss of face in a possible ugly confrontation, the general had only two of his trusted officers present.

The conversation began with superficial comments on details of a big upcoming conference organized by the government on the matter of Thuong highlanders. Then, wasting no time, Tacelosky bluntly broached the subject. "General Hunting has already told me what I need to know. There's nothing about your plan to object to, but I'd like to discuss a few details."

Here again was the word "but," the word that always marked the beginning and the end of Tacelosky's manipulative argument on any issue, as the general knew only too well. In the past, General Tri had characteristically yielded on a few issues so reconciliation could prevail. As the present discussion unfolded, the general again yielded on a few points. But the American officer seemed to expect him to concede something more, the nature of which he could not guess and was anxious to know. The general tried to narrow down the issue, which he already considered to have been well focused.

"Mr. Tacelosky," said the general in irritation. "We have completely worked out an operational plan. The American help we need is fifty helicopter flights for troop insertion and the evacuation. This morning, I discussed the matter with General Hunting over the phone, and he agreed in principle to this plan."

Interrupting General Tri, Tacelosky steered the discussion into a different direction. "Do you know, General, what policy it was that resulted in the present dilemma at Dakto? Formerly, Dakto was a secure area with a very well established Special Forces camp. Since the day General Thuyet drove courageous Thuong soldiers to the other side of the border, it has become the worst sector, an area completely beyond the control of the GVN. General Thuyet made many such mistakes in the highlands, and now you have to bear the consequences. History is continuous development, not a matter of recurrence or repetition. As I see it, the day will come when autonomy for the highlands must be conceded. It's inevitable."

Was this Special Forces talking or the CIA? It certainly could not be denied that General Thuyet had made mistakes, and he had paid for this by being transferred to another location. Though he did not agree with General Thuyet on some issues, and would not act as General Thuyet had, General Tri secretly admired his predecessor's strength and straightforward actions. He asked himself how much longer he would have to walk a tightrope. Seemingly in the present situation the rope had suddenly burst aflame. Only forty-eight hours were left to carry the operation through the last and most crucial step, too short a time to spar with this American official's diversionary tactics.

"Mr. Tacelosky," the general again said with exasperation, "please remember that we have less than forty-eight hours to execute the many stages of this operation."

While anxiety dominated General Tri's demeanor, Tacelosky maintained the calm facial expression of a shameless sadist. Abruptly, he exposed his last card.

"Dakto has to be considered a typical case, one that must be handled in a manner that applies to all other mountainous villages. I agree that, if there were adequate means of transportation, you would be able to bring those few hundred villagers here. But what will happen after that? Forcing them to give up their homes and their domestic animals, then throwing them into refugee camps where they will ruminate like creatures in a zoo, is what we Americans don't want to see happen. We have constantly had to listen to the refugees' complaints that even though the committed economic aid has been more than adequate, much of it has never reached them. Have you ever questioned the responsible Vietnamese officers and officials concerning this matter?"

General Tri began to feel insulted by the presumptiveness and rude words of this American who had just changed hats and was now speaking from his USAID role, a man whose thick facial skin was pockmarked, who wore an expression revealing no feeling, no emotion. The general again wondered how the situation would have turned out if General Thuyet had been in his place. Undoubtedly, General Thuyet would never have allowed Tacelosky to voice such impertinent comments and questions. Had it not been for his own wife's insatiable engagement in various black-market dealings and other gaffes, which he was sure were known to the Americans—a fact that Tacelosky had just indirectly reminded him of—General Tri would have stood up to the American official once and for all. Unfortunately, he now found himself in a very tight spot. All he could do was walk the tightrope a short while longer and await a change in the circumstance.

The general managed to come up with an amiable response to the American. "We quite agree that it is necessary to improve the condition of the refugee camps. But that requires time. The urgent matter right now is to expeditiously liberate innocent people from the area before the VC force them to leave in a different direction."

As if this were a dialogue between two deaf persons, Tacelosky continued his own separate path of discourse. "General, why don't you think it advisable to entrust to these same Thuong people the organization and distribution of material relief? All the Thuong need to do is directly contact our advisory group, and in that way your staff won't be blamed for any unfortunate occurrence or accused of mishandling relief provided by USAID.

"Also, in the matter of protecting highlanders from the communists, training and supporting Thuong soldiers is something that should be done, and I don't understand why you people are dead set against it. The crux of the matter is we are fighting a war for the hearts and the minds of the people. Since you Vietnamese have failed to gain the trust of the Thuong people, I think it's only reasonable that you leave us alone to do that job with utmost care."

Tacelosky spoke at length to General Tri on this subject and seemed not the least troubled by the passage of time. Throughout the meal, the general did his best to gracefully endure the humiliation. Afterwards came a short briefing on the planned operation. Upon leaving, the American official gave assurances to the Vietnamese general. "I will meet with General Hunting this very afternoon to discuss how we can help with your operation. I promise you that I will try my best to work out something within the limits of what America can provide in the way of air support."

General Tri could not be optimistic on the basis of such a vague promise. He immediately summoned his staff. An alternative strategy was worked out in the event no airlift support operation was mounted by the Americans. At the same time, he again tried to contact General Hunting in the hope of obtaining direct help from the American general.

CHAPTER SIX

The two-stage operation to liberate Dakto was carried out quite successfully: an insertion of troops for defensive blocking followed by evacuation of the threatened Thuong. General Tri was a very happy man, for success was achieved in spite of Tacelosky's intended obstruction. The general had not expected that a mere journalist like Davis could help him so effectively. In fact, being a close friend of General Hunting, Davis just in the nick of time had intervened and informed the American general of the troublesome political game in which Tacelosky had engaged. More than six hundred villagers were safely evacuated to a resettlement center. In a furious state, Tacelosky left for Saigon. Also through Davis, General Tri secured the Denmans' help in obtaining material supplies for the villagers. Tension had been obvious in the various conflicts between American military personnel and civilian advisors, typified by the different ways of approaching a solution to the Dakto problem that General Hunting and Tacelosky proposed.

Davis planned to return to Saigon, but I wanted to remain a few more days to explore mountainous villages nearby and most especially to visit those resettlement camps the American press claimed to be no better than places where animals were abused. I myself was not surprised by the shortage of food and clothing at the present resettlement center. I had witnessed the same miserable conditions a few weeks earlier at camps like Chu Lai and Lệ Mỹ.

My gathering of materials for a new report on the highlands was nearly complete. The findings revealed several complicated angles I had not clearly seen before. For example, there was no such thing as a uniform Thuong race. Rather, the actual circumstance was the proximity of more than thirty ethnic tribes living together whose basic interests were often in conflict with one another. The suggestion that the Thuong themselves should be allowed to manage their own affairs in the highlands posed even more problems than it could solve. Living together in an underdeveloped social environment like Vietnam, Thuong people were still about a century behind modern civilization. The idea of an independent nation called *Dega*, for "Sons of the Mountains," as the term translates, was no more than a product of the Thuong's innocence, contaminated by close contact with the American Green Berets. Almost thirty years ago, an autonomous Cochinchina had been initiated when this southern part of Vietnam had been thoroughly trampled upon by French soldiers. History was not a continuous development as Tacelosky had said. It was more like repetitions of the same event under different circumstances.

On my last day in the area, I was invited to dinner by Major Y Ksor. Another dinner guest was Nay Ry, a young progressive Thuong intellectual. He was one among a handful of educated Thuong persons. He had gone to Lycée Yersin in Dalat, then attended the Institute of National Administration, from which he graduated first in the specialized field of "highlands affairs." Subsequently, he was able to spend several years studying in

America. An ethnic Djarai, Nay Ry was a personality respected by all sides: the government, the Americans, the Thuong separatist fighters. He was completing a book based upon research on the question of ethnic minorities, a book intended to counter French and American scholars had presented, which Nay Ry judged to be full of misconceptions.

When asked about the racial factor governing various rebellious movements, his expressed view was very clearly stated. "In the whole world today, no people can boast purity of their blood line. It is not logical to introduce a racial element into the struggle. Look at the United States of America. There you can find numerous racial groups gathered which have joined together to form a strong nation, while still maintaining their respective unique customs and practices. Even the civilized, though rather divided, Europe is trying to become a united entity. So, one cannot be the least surprised that a tiny country like Vietnam is struggling even harder to become united. When Vietnam has to seek alliance with the larger Southeast Asian community in order to survive the threat from mainland China, with its population of 700 million, how can she afford to be torn and divided by racial conflict?"

For a Thuong person to be capable of having such a view and stating it well, Nay Ry could be considered erudite. He discussed at great length the future of a global polity, from which Vietnam as a whole and those struggling for a separate *Dega* nation could not detach themselves.

Y Ksor offered his view regarding the reasons behind unrest in the highlands. "Aside from the government's neglect to improve the life of ethnic minority peoples, I think we should take into account the main purpose of the Americans in this affair. I experienced the same kind of manipulation in the hands of the French in the past."

He went on to relate that before boarding their ships to leave Vietnam in 1954, the French had secretly incited the Thuong to demand highland autonomy. In fact, the French, including rubber plantation owners, had had a hand in the FULRO movement. Y Ksor himself had been approached by the French to work toward that goal.

Following from Y Ksor's argument, Nay Ry presented a sharp observation. "In my opinion," he said, "we should first ask ourselves if the main responsibility does not rest with us. Accusations have been heaped upon the Americans, as if they were instrumental in creating opposing sides in regional and religious conflicts, most specifically that they incited Thuong rebellions in the Central Highlands. But have we ever looked closely at our own weakness? If we were strong and united, neither the French nor the American presence would make any difference to the problems we face. Therefore, I don't quite agree with the tough attitude of General Thuyet, leading to anti-American sentiments. The anti-American stand is not the way by which we can resolve the difficulties in the Central Highlands."

Y Ksor appeared not to be in complete agreement with Nay Ry's idealistic attitude. "Listen," he said in a firm tone of voice, "the responsibility is not simply on the mental level. The Americans have had their hands in the whole Thuong affair, an involvement marked with the blood of innocent people on both sides of the conflict. An American like Tacelosky can in no way be considered a friend when he was willing to sacrifice all members of a village for his own political scheme."

Atypical of youth's fierce argumentative tendency, Nay Ry proved moderate in his attempt to mollify the silver-haired major. "Major," he said quietly, "extremism can't lead us anywhere. Why do we judge the Americans through the obnoxious face of Tacelosky alone, and not through a good journalist like Davis or through the Denmans? I think we should be practical. As regards a development program for highlanders, now or in the future, we cannot do without a contribution from the Americans."

I joked with Nay Ry. "Those individuals are different because Denman is a minister and Davis has been Asianized."

"That's not true," Nay Ry replied. "The years I spent studying in America showed me that not all Americans are like the Special Forces soldiers leading their adventurous life here. In the same way, not all of us Thuong people are easily incited and tempted. I myself was one of those who founded and pursued the highlands struggle. I also tried my best to curb the group's excessiveness, even as it labeled me a traitor, labeled me as one going against them. My view is very clear: to fight for the Thuong's right to progress is a legitimate action, but to turn that struggle into a venture of hatred and enmity is unacceptable. Wise as the French were, they had to give up their selfish design for the fate of the highlands. The Americans are an immense ocean away from us. How can we really know them? How can we trust them with our lives? Better than anyone else, we understand that in the final analysis we must get along well with the lowland Vietnamese in order to survive and hopefully progress."

I asked Nay Ry how much truth was expressed in the published summary of aspirations held by the separatist side. He replied succinctly. "A different flag, a separate army, a separatist *Dega* nation, all these things are not essential aspirations of your Thuong fellow countrymen. As for other demands stated in the summary, they are not different from those listed at the conclusion of the last Thuong conference. For example, they demand that the government establish a Department of Thuong Affairs, allocate an adequate number of Thuong representatives to the National Assembly, build more schools and retain the teaching of tribal languages, return to highlanders the land that was taken from them, allow for the reestablishment of legal courts based on Thuong customs, and so on. Those are reasonable demands that are not difficult for the government to immediately comply with in order to pacify the separatists. The most outstanding characteristic of us simple Thuong is that we are quick to believe in you, and equally quick to doubt you unless you give us positive proof of your truthfulness. As one of our proverbs states: 'When the right hand promises something, the left hand has to honor it immediately.'"

In the middle of our meal, a younger Thuong man appeared in the company of an elderly Thuong man. The younger individual was the same Thuong whose truthfulness had been guaranteed to General Tri by Y Ksor upon the honor of his rank. The older man was the chief of the village of Dakto who came to express his gratitude to the major for his attentive care and help in the liberation of the villagers. They brought him as presents an ivory statue and a most beautiful crossbow with accompanying arrows.

Looking toward me, Y Ksor immediately said to them, "I only did my duty; as much as could be done, given my position. The real help was provided by the reporter here. Did you hear that, Mr. Reporter? We Thuong people are simple folk who are grateful to those who help us. Please accept both these gifts and consider that they represent a token of my gratitude."

Knowing that one should not be formal with the Thuong, I gracefully accepted the gifts and explained to them the role of Davis.

"Actually, this whole affair was settled thanks to the journalist Davis, who is close to General Hunting at An Khe. I just happened to talk to Davis about the dilemma we faced here, and did not expect such wholehearted assistance from him."

Y Ksor told us of his first impressions when meeting Davis. "He is the first American journalist I've met whom I like. Most other foreign press people are rude and insolent, showing no respect to anyone. On top of that, the news items they produce exhibit ill will toward us."

Nay Ry shared with us his knowledge of the American media. "That's precisely why the American people misunderstand Vietnam," he said. "Their system of communication is as fast as lightning. News items are transmitted before they are verified, even when they happen within the U.S.A., which leads to harmful assessments. If a black person is shot dead in Chicago, only five minutes later the whole country knows about it, and each person is free to interpret the event according to his own viewpoint. Machinery and technological progress have made public opinion all over the world a Pavlovian conditioned response. In my opinion, we should blame our poor mass communications and our press. How can we blame the American press, when we rely on foreign news agencies for information about our own national news? Recently, a student paper criticized the Vietnamese press for such reliance, and I quite agree with that criticism. Blame oneself first before reproaching others, as the saying goes."

Nay Ry strongly impressed me at this first meeting. I told myself that I would try to persuade General Tri or General Thuyet to try to find suitable roles for talented Thuong in all future programs.

The major turned to the younger Thuong man and made an inquiry. "How are your wife and baby?"

"My baby is fine. My wife is all right now after the surgery. At first I was worried that she would die."

The Major turned to me. "You see, Mr. Reporter, even in this day and age, Thuong people still rely on herbal medicine to cure sickness. As for birthing, Thuong women, like this man's wife, give birth standing up holding onto a pillar. This man's baby came out so fast, falling to the ground dragging down the mother's uterus. It was fortunate that she gave birth here. Had it happened in Dakto, mother and child would have died."

Nay Ry seemed always to come up with a different idea. "The issue," he commented, "is not simply to provide ethnic peoples with doctors and adequate medicine. The main thing is to educate them so they will come to believe in the usefulness of modern technology, and thus want to adapt themselves to the new circumstances. Therefore, the initial difficulty is to find a way to implement compulsory education for everyone."

An enthusiastic social activist, Nay Ry held a farsighted view of all issues, addressing fundamental questions. His wide and heavy face obscured his intellectualism, a healthy intellectualism in every sense of the word.

The conversation went on late into the night, facilitated by frothy rice wine and delicious food.

The path of red earth leading back to the hotel was splashed with puddles of water edged in frost. The rice wine kept my body warm, as drunkenness settled into wobbly legs of rubber. I decided I would go to Dalat tomorrow even though Như Nguyện might not be there. I had tried to telephone twice, but had not been able to reach her. Keeping my reservations at the Grand Hotel, I hung onto a thin hope that she awaited me still near a stand of mountain pines.

CHAPTER SEVEN

Not returning to Saigon as planned, Davis suggested the two of us go together the next day to Ban Me Thuot to attend the big conference on Thuong highlanders organized by General Tri. Though prepared in haste, the conference was nonetheless to be complete, with all expected rituals and festivities.

Besides the prime minister, who was a general, present at the opening ceremony were many important members of the foreign diplomatic corps, including the American ambassador. General Tri thus appeared to be successful with his flexible reconciliation policy, as opposed to the failed hard line taken by General Thuyet. Once again were repeated the sacrifice of a buffalo during the oath-taking ceremony and other rituals designed to demonstrate Thuong loyalty to the Saigon government. It was a rare occasion, which saw gathered together representatives of the more than thirty ethnic groups scattered over the national territory. Major Y Ksor was credited with arranging the meeting in an effort to work toward reconciliation with the Kinh.

The audience's attention was particularly drawn to the lecture presented in a tone laden with sadness and emotion by Nay Ry, the young Thuong intellectual. He expressed the desperate wish of the highlanders to live peacefully in the Kinh-Thuong community and the necessity of protecting territorial integrity.

Every wound is a tragedy when rendered in the refined language of literature, I thought, mulling over Nay Ry's eloquent speech. Indeed, as he pointed out, through the many ups and downs of history, through many dramatic changes, no Thuong person had remained an integrated being. During this war that had dragged on for twenty-five years, there existed also the residue of a tragedy and of a political plot of earlier origin that had lingered on for a century and affected the life of the highlanders. I wondered how much more blood and tears were to be shed before a better life would prevail in the Central Highlands. The dim, lusterless figure of General Tri among a crowd of American Green Beret soldiers failed to enliven that hope for the future. I thought of General Thuyet, who was now controlling I Corps, and of legends surrounding his rule with an iron hand wrapped in velvet. It seemed that he was a necessary element in the eyes of those who nurtured the dream of realizing such hope.

Before returning to Saigon, General Tri mobilized a platoon of well-seasoned Rhadé soldiers to drive out game animals from the deep jungle to be hunted by the government delegation. The prime minister was known to be fond of tiger hunting. Powerless tigers were chased toward awaiting rifles. The lieutenant colonel, who continued to be assigned to the Psychological Warfare Bureau, stayed close to the prime minister and tried to express his deep concern for the Promised Land—a land which, in his view, was in danger. When telling me about the encounter later, the colonel could not hide the bitterness revealed in his tone of voice, made poignant by humor.

"The prime minister thinks thick jungle is as wide open as the blue sky," the colonel announced with a scoff. "So he said that when peace returns, he would need only two hours to wipe out the Thuong rebels, a separatist force that he does not think worth serious consideration. I must say that I am disappointed, truly disappointed, because more than anyone else I know clearly how dangerous the situation is. It's not only the Green Berets; it's also agents of the CIA who are trampling upon the highlands.

"All the good and bad events that have occurred here cannot be attributed solely to Kinh-Thuong antagonism. These Americans are by no means discreet. We know that they openly enticed Thuong people, inviting them to their residences and telling them without mincing words that the Vietnamese, communist or not, were out to find a way to destroy ethnic minorities. As such, the only course left for the Thuong was to pursue their separatist movement all the way to the end. Mr. Reporter, do you know who said this to them? It was not Tacelosky. The words came from Minister Denman. Denman did not suspect that among those whom he thought had sold out, there were some of our own people. After they left the meeting, they recounted to me everything said."

"That's hard to believe," I exclaimed. "Even Y Ksor reveres the minister."

My doubt aroused the colonel, who at once energetically offered his analysis and backed it up with what he considered evidence.

"I know," he said. "I would think the same as you do, if I only looked at his minister's robes and the social services he's outwardly engaged in. But the truth is very different than the appearance, a truth that I am sure even General Thuyet is not aware of. The dangerous element in highlands separatism is not the cruel Tacelosky; rather, it lies in the cool and calculating mind of Old Denman. Perhaps it's beyond your imagination to consider that he is the hidden manipulator behind all the letters and documents issued by the separatist side. As for Major Y Ksor, it's understandable that, as a Christian, he reveres the minister, but the reverence is largely religious in nature."

"How about the role of French Catholic priests?" I asked.

"Of course they are still liked by the Thuong, but they presently can't do much to gain a foothold in the highlands, even with support from the French Horticultural Society, one of the traditional vehicles. The point is, the Thuong are very practically minded, and this practical orientation corresponds with American politics, a politics that is the politics of the rich. Therefore, the Americans have no difficulty in overpowering the hundred-year-old French influence on the highlanders.

"In conflict with the Americans, and determined to get even with them, French plantation owners have flirted with the communist guerrillas, and reached a compromise, so that the most secure area these days is within the region of the rubber plantations. The communists' former mortal enemies have suddenly become their close allies."

I thought over his explanation, then asked about the Americans' ultimate goal with regard to the highlands. The colonel's observation seemed to be derived from unquestionable beliefs. He answered without hesitation.

"The more than sixty SFOBs—Special Forces Operational Bases—have been like myriad good bait thrown into a wasteland short on food supplies. Once established, they quickly attracted Thuong people, who flocked to them like swarms of ants. Most of the Thuong who gathered at these bases were fed by the Americans and then recruited into the CIDG, Civilian Irregular Defense Group. This group has been, and remains, completely beyond the control of our government.

"These bases are like boxes of gunpowder ready to explode when touched by a spark from the nearby fire. On a certain fine day, when the Americans fan the fire producing these tiny sparks, we will be faced with a *fait accompli* beyond salvage. It's possible that then a referendum will be held under international supervision. And you already know for sure what the results of that will be."

"What results?"

"Given that we have experienced the demise of President Diem's regime, the collapse of South Vietnam is only a matter of time—because the U.S. is about to return Okinawa to Japan, Clark Air Force Base to the Philippines, and also leave other strategic locations. However, even if they were to lose Saigon, the Americans would still have all the territory from the seventeenth parallel to Đồng Xoài, within which are Da Nang, Chu Lai, and especially Cam Ranh Bay Naval Base.

"Only when you see with your own eyes the infrastructure built by the Americans at this port facility can you understand the nature of their far-reaching vision. They are investing for a hundred years of work to come, during which stretch of time they can only count on the loyal and long-lasting collaboration of Thuong people. According to information provided by intelligence sources, there is in Phnom Penh a network of espionage which reaches out to recruit even disgruntled Thuong communist leaders."

Not exactly incredulous, I still laughed, then commented that his scenario sounded like a deluded espionage agent's tasking, an impossible mission. This reaction prompted further elaboration on his part.

"Look," he asserted, "the CIA is precisely an organization specialized in carrying out impossible missions like that. Their aims and ideas are sometimes quite silly, but given their crafty maneuvering and limitless financial capacity, they have been successful in many places around the world. As regards the highlands here, with the willing submission of the Thuong, I can guarantee you that it will take a long time before any sign of weariness is detected in the ambitions of a number of strategically placed Americans."

The colonel appeared truly worried about what he called the game of destruction and rebuilding played by sorcerers like Old Denman. As regards the present, he believed there were signs of movement, movement like that of dark clouds forewarning of a storm, a storm which in this case would demand more blood and tears before any good future for the highlands could be hoped for.

The colonel's daughter invited us to partake of dinner. As she carried in a heavy tray of food, my attention was on her soft white hands, which were like young bamboo shoots with fingers tapering at the end. In a dark land covered with red dust, it was indeed rare to find a beautiful white-skinned young woman like this.

The colonel said, "You have come to the highlands many times, but this is the first time I have had the honor of inviting you, Mr. Reporter, to a meal in the southern style prepared by my daughter. For this special occasion, we have an exceptional wine made from dark red glutinous rice. One gets rather tired of drinking whiskey and the common local rice wine. Let's drink to your health, Mr. Reporter."

In his rather humble family surroundings, the colonel treated me with all the openness and simplicity characteristic of southern people, who are known for their sincerely deep sentiments. In great spirits from the sweet influence of good wine, the colonel joked that he would give his daughter to me in marriage, which made her blush with embarrassment. She represented the beautiful image of the traditional ideal woman that any man would dream of having as his wife. In moments of emptiness in life, one truly feels the need of a woman's gentle and soothing hands, I thought.

"To be posted anywhere is fine with me," said the colonel. "But when my daughter enters university, I don't want to live far from her. It seems that she wants to take an entrance examination to the College of Fine Arts."

"After Tet, I will temporarily cease to be a journalist. I have accepted a teaching position at the College of Fine Arts in Hue. If you are transferred to I Corps, Colonel, you may want to send her to study there."

The Colonel was very surprised to learn that I was formerly a painter. I told him that even though I was to become a professor of fine arts, I did not have much faith in the result of teaching. I did not mention that Như Nguyện was the true motivation for my decision to join academia.

"Then I hope to see you again in Hue," the colonel said.

"Oh, you already know where your next station is to be?" I asked.

"General Tri wanted to send me back to the Ministry of National Defense. But I managed to get in contact with General Thuyet, and he agreed to have me transferred to I Corps, near the seventeenth parallel where fierce battles are being waged. My attitude has been clear: either I am to be discharged from the army and engage in teaching, or, if I am to stay in the army, I am to perform services compatible with my ability and position. I am sure I won't be disappointed when working with General Thuyet."

Once again, I realized that for many people General Thuyet was irreplaceable and important for the future development of the highlands.

A dog barked. I turned my head and, at the gate, caught sight of the robe of a Buddhist monk.

Without waiting for an introduction, I recognized Giác Nghiệp, a young monk from *Phương Bối Am*, "Palm Leaf Sanctuary." He had been a luminary during the period of Buddhist struggle in the early 1960s. Subsequently, he withdrew from the limelight, quietly and patiently resuming his religious path and committing himself to social work. Even though Giác Nghiệp revered superior monk Pháp Viên as his master, he himself seemed to possess greater religious demeanor.

It was curious that the colonel, who admired the late Catholic President Diem, could at the same time become close friends with a monk who had fought to topple his hero. Their conversation flowed easily in all friendliness, and they seemed to be compatible with each other.

Giác Nghiệp was the opposite of his own master in several ways. While the incisively sharp manner of arguing and the ardent emotional responses of monk Pháp Viên won him admiration, Giác Nghiệp had a Taoist way of talking, natural and calm, which touched people's hearts. Even though he had spent many years at an American university, he showed no sign of having been Westernized. Instead, he blended well in his native cultural landscape. Giác Nghiệp was a poet who sang of the beauty of the countryside, who preferred the physical labor of rural life to sedentary employment in big cities.

He was also a theorist among a group of progressive monks who leaned toward modernization of Buddhism. Very concerned with social problems, he had looked for a field of social action in which young monk students could become engaged. It was not monk Giác Nghiệp himself, but the colonel who proudly told me about the projects that those at Palm Leaf Sanctuary had accomplished.

"You know," the colonel said to me, "barely a year has passed since its founding, but were you to visit that sanctuary you would be surprised to witness a model agricultural farm in action. On one occasion, I reported this to General Thuyet and commented that the organization of mountainous Hdip Mrao villages could benefit from being modeled after Palm Leaf Sanctuary. But . . ."

The colonel did not finish his sentence. I read his thought, however. This precise model had aroused suspicion from the authorities toward Buddhism, leading to a situation of near non-cooperation.

Making no blame or criticism, Giác Nghiệp optimistically observed, "Though security factors limit areas of operation, I think there are still very good locations for experimentation. Palm Leaf Sanctuary is but the first pilot project, undertaken by monks with the poorest of means. It takes the form of *kibbutzim,* but not without appropriate modifications. In my opinion, when peace returns, with almost a million men discharged from the army and with an equivalent number of unemployed workers, the highlands will be the Promised Land, as it can be a base for the postwar economy and serve to balance the array of population densities all over the country. I have already sent a petition concerning this matter to Mr. Lilienthal in Saigon, and I am hoping to get attention from his Committee for Postwar Economic Development."

The name Lilienthal seemed unknown to the colonel. As for me, I knew that present in that committee, a U.S.-sponsored agency, was the law professor who was a very close advisor of General Thuyet.

I explained. "Lilienthal is an American well-known for his economic plans for developing countries, among which the greatest success was a development project carried out in southwest Iran. One hopes he will now bring a similar miracle to Vietnam."

Giác Nghiệp smiled, a sincere tolerant smile devoid of irony or sarcasm. Calmly, he said, "Whatever project we are talking about, it will not be done without workers or the industrious hands of the Vietnamese people."

When getting up to leave, Giác Nghiệp thoughtfully invited me to visit Palm Leaf Sanctuary and, if possible, to live there for awhile. This first meeting with the monk left me with a most pure, untroubled, and pleasant feeling.

CHAPTER EIGHT

Absent Như Nguyện, my two days in Dalat were spent in longing and sadness. The night grew so cold that I could not sleep, got up, worked until well past the midnight hour. Wind howled through trees of the pine wood, moved up hills, rattled doors. Suddenly, there was the thought that Như Nguyện did not care for me any longer.

I went back to Saigon, report on the highlands just completed in hand. After delivering it to the newspaper's office, I sped to Như Nguyện's home looking for her. Three days ago, the old servant informed me, she had left for Geneva. Left without leaving me a note! Her house stood empty, indifferent.

She had gone.

She had returned me to my work as a journalist.

At this point, the story of a Green Belt of defense, which had begun to formulate in my mind with the 1964 Thuong rebellion, was no longer merely a hypothesis. The data accumulated over the years, especially during my last journey, had confirmed the hypothesis, or rather, established it as a real fact to contend with. This fact was that a chain of American SFOBs, stoutly supported by cooperating ethnic groups in Vietnam, Laos, and the north of Burma, was being strung out as a strategic defensive belt to keep out the Chinese and prevent communism from spreading southward to mainland Southeast Asia.

For the time being, I was not in the right state of mind to even begin writing the first chapter of the intended book. Nonetheless, out of habit, every day, I tried to fill up two pages with words. I jotted down issues identified, noted ideas as they came. Only at such moments did I experience the feeling of rest—rest through following real life as though it were the development of a novel. And all the more so because it was filled with tragedies, with adversities beyond imagination!

The first period of my journalistic career had offered me so many rich life experiences, but what had I managed to record? From empty and dull personal responses, I moved toward ambition for a great intellectual adventure. Life was no longer a succession of passing scenes and events; it was an uninterrupted chain of thoughts.

Since Như Nguyện's appearance, my life had been touched by ferment. The days after her departure were endured in mental and emotional crisis. I could write nothing for a short time, nothing other than memories and recollections. Crisis, when no stimulus to the creative impulse, is truly destructive. These were the last words I wrote during this period of emptiness.

The window framed an afternoon's sky, showed a deep blue parted by green-leafed branches hovering in a stilled wind that highlighted street noises, life's noises. I wished for quietude, a place within, somewhere to dwell on the days I would spend in Hue, on all the promising excitements there would be there.

It had, in fact, been from Hue that Mr. Hoang Thai Trung had sent me additional information after several of my articles on the highlands had been published. I was very interested in the materials sent, in this painstaking research work of his. It dealt with the issue of Thuong people throughout history, with the collapse of close cooperation between Kinh and Thuong and the loss of their mutual contribution to the history of Vietnam because of the divide-and-rule policy of the French.

Recognizing that Kinh-Thuong unity was a threat to their rule, the French prevented lowland Vietnamese from mixing with highlanders—indeed, forbade all communication between them. The French considered the Thuong a subhuman species on the verge of extinction. Thuong were regarded as antique items, curiosities needing preservation in their original shape and form. The Thuong problem, starting from there, was subsequently exacerbated by the American Green Berets in their desire to go the last part of the way.

Mr. Trung's point of view was in opposition to the distorted perspective presented in Minister Denman's book. Denman, as well as a number of other foreign scholars, argued for a breaking up, a historical separation among ethnic groups living in Southeast Asia. This view of theirs was arguably an explanation for the ongoing upheavals and conflicts in the area. Aside from the research papers of Mr. Trung, I found not one serious Vietnamese publication reasonably to be considered a basis for my study.

I paid Davis a personal visit, bringing along the presents from the villagers of Dakto. Arriving just after Professor Ross had left, I noted empty bottles of '33' Beer scattered on a table imprinted with dark rings from wet glasses. As expected, Davis delightedly chose the crossbow and arrows, leaving me the ivory statue—which I thought I would give Như Nguyện when she returned from Geneva. The crossbow was immediately mounted on the unfettered expanse of white wall facing, on the opposite wall, one of my two paintings that Davis had bought. This painting, entitled "Serenity," featured a composed young lady under a new moon.

"Davis," I said, "Y Ksor made the observation that you are not like any other American."

Smiling in all modesty, Davis replied, "Maybe that's why Dr. Ross criticized me. He said I have lived in Vietnam for so long that I have adopted too many Asian traits."

I smiled in return.

Turning serious, he observed, "The intervention with General Hunting has left me with a lot of trouble."

Recalling Tacelosky's anger, I responded instantly. "Tacelosky is the only one who has set himself against your good deed. But never mind that. Your having saved more than six hundred villagers' lives has won their profound gratitude."

"I wouldn't be concerned if Tacelosky was the only one involved. Triet, you know me. Once I have decided to do something, I don't back down because of opposition from someone like Tacelosky, opposition that has only one reason: that what I intend to do will hurt their individual personal interests. But in this case, Ross criticized me in terms of other concerns, like my loyalty to my country, or consideration for the sacrifice being made by America in this war. He said I act like an outsider, not an American. This is something that I can't help pondering upon."

Truly, just as Dr. Ross had observed, the Davis sitting across from me at present was not a pure American full of self-satisfaction, but a quiet person dealing with many unanswered questions. In a cold tone of voice he related Dr. Ross's arguments.

"Ross said that even though I now live in the middle of an Asia at war, full of betrayals and ingratitude, I cannot escape the fact that I am an American with blond hair and blue eyes, that no matter how many years I stay here, I will never share the qualities endowed by their yellow skin, their black hair, and their black eyes. I absolutely don't agree with Ross's view on this. In fact, it is from my long experience of living in Asia that I clearly see the reason for America's failure here. I have often told Ross that Americans should have considered themselves guests in this foreign land. The matter of saving one's face may not be of concern in America, but with Asians it may well be an issue of life and death. I told him that Americans would sorely fail if they insisted on acting as if they owned this country and forced local people to comply with their ideas. The myth of a civilizing mission or a manifest destiny can no longer be tolerated by Asians whose own civilization has a tradition older than the history of the United States of America."

I reminded Davis of an item released by the AP news agency relating an accusation made by an Argentinean paper concerning intervention by American Green Berets to help the rebellious side overthrow the government.

Davis laughed. "That's no different from what's going on here in the Central Highlands. Some Americans, who pride themselves on a thorough knowledge of the global situation, believe that they can effectively engage in unconventional warfare in a manner that disregards basic agreements made with their allies. Understanding that, you will not be surprised to learn of conflicts like those in Argentina. In my opinion, it's time for America to definitely make a choice between its allies and short-term self-interest, if it doesn't want to lose everything."

"Why is Dr. Ross concerned about what you did," I asked, "especially given that he does not at all like Tacelosky?"

"There's nothing here officially under his authority; neither is there anything that escapes his attention and concern. As I understand it, Ross exerts a lot of influence not only on the American Embassy here in Vietnam, but also on people with power back in Washington."

I looked at Davis. He was tall and thin, an enduring bamboo stalk lost on the Asian continent, a landscape enveloped in the foul airs of unrest and war.

He got up and went to the bar, asking me the habitual question, "Cognac and soda?"

I smiled and nodded my acceptance. "Listen, Davis," I said, "the elderly man who is the village chief in Dakto is anxiously waiting to invite you for a drink. You will be served a very delicious and specially distilled rice wine contained in a jar from which both guest and host drink through a long tube."

"I know about that. Actually, I took the opportunity to enjoy the indigenous rice wine a couple of times in the past, while going along with the French on military operations."

Almost forty, Davis had spent half his life involved with this war. He understood Vietnam and Asia well, in the true sense of deep understanding of the peoples and cultures of the continent.

I reiterated an oft-repeated observation. "Those who know you think you are more Oriental than contemporary Asians."

"As I have said, part of Ross's criticism of me is exactly on that point, which I consider something I can be proud of. I previously had misconceptions about him. Now I realize that his view of the world doesn't extend beyond the narrow window framing his mind. He can't perceive the fresh blue sky of Asia. Living here all these long years, I have been greatly influenced by the profound Buddhist teachings and by the sublime Taoist philosophy of unassertive action, though I remain an adherent of Christianity."

"I seem to remember that you can read and speak Chinese."

"Unfortunately, a big disadvantage for me in my attempt to understand Eastern civilization is that I can't read Chinese, even though during my years in China I learned to speak Mandarin, a beautiful language that sounds like a song with full rhythm and melody. I also managed a few sentences in Cantonese. Because I can't read Chinese, I have to depend on research books written by Western scholars, which I believe contain many distorted interpretations, as well as biases."

"By the way," Davis continued, changing direction, "I am told that monk Pháp Viên is an excellent theologian, and in terms of religious rank he is considered a superior monk. I'd like to get acquainted with him, not in my capacity as a journalist, but simply in the hope of being guided by him on the path to enlightenment. Do I understand correctly that you maintain a close relationship with him?"

In truth, I knew well the ways of monk Pháp Viên. He lived in profound quietude and meditation, preferring to stay away from the limelight, especially in connection with the press. But Davis might be the type of person that the monk would like to meet.

"Monk Pháp Viên," I answered, "is very good in classical Chinese and Sanskrit, but he is not familiar with modern foreign languages. That lack is a major hindrance in his efforts to find a suitable way to conciliate with Western thought. Because of this, a number of uninformed American journalists think that he exhibits a xenophobic attitude. At present, as a protective measure by the Saigon government, he is in isolation under what amounts to house arrest.

"When he returns to his pagoda, I will introduce you, so that the two of you can play chess together. As a highly skilled player, he will be able to understand clearly your character just by watching your moves and your way of getting out of a stalemate. He is possessed of a very artistic mind. The good relationship between him and myself certainly does not stem from the fact that I am a sympathetic journalist, but because he knows I was formerly a painter.

"Incidentally, I have concluded that the Vietnamese press currently is at a stifling impasse. I am planning to return to the

brush and easel, and for that reason I have agreed to teach after
Tet at the College of Fine Arts in Hue."

Davis laughed with pleasure and reminded me of what he had
said the first time we met. "Triet, see what I told you? I said sooner or later you would return to painting, because you are a true
painter. I have always wanted to lead the life of an artist like you.
This has been a dream I've nurtured since childhood, but have not
been capable of realizing, which leaves me no choice but to continue making a living in journalism."

"But you are gloriously successful in this career, even if it
was not predestined by desire. You've achieved the ultimate goal,
which is the dream of all beginners."

Our mutual praise of each other's accomplishments had gone
beyond ordinary politeness. Davis seemed sincerely happy with
my comments. He picked up a telegram from his desk and
showed it to me.

"It is clear that images of the pain and suffering caused by
war in Vietnam are still popular. Just before you arrived, I
received this cable from Hong Kong informing me that the
International Association of Journalistic Photography has decided to give this year's award to me for the photos I took of the
large battles that transpired in the highlands during the rainy season. The Vietnam War has treated me so generously. Glory associated with blood and tears is such an irony. Perhaps I will ask to
be transferred to our Paris bureau, where I can begin writing
books on Vietnam—something I have long desired to do."

"So, when are you going to Paris?"

"Not now. That will have to wait for a while, as it may take a
year to find someone who can replace me here. As you know,
Vietnam is still a focal point in international news."

The fact that Davis's presence in Vietnam was necessary to
his paper prompted me to think of the situation of Phuong Nghi,
a widow who was my acquaintance. Given her skill in English,

there would be no problem in communication, and I wanted to introduce her to Davis.

"Listen, Davis," I said, "if you are interested, you can have an assistant who can help you with your demanding work here. I know one who is capable. This woman's fiancé, a young army doctor, has just been killed in a battle near Da Nang. She had a child with him, and as you can imagine, she is in a difficult situation. I believe that she can efficiently assist you, and this will help her make a living."

"Yes, of course, bring her here. Even if she doesn't want to work for the paper, I think I can introduce her to some other kind of job suitable to her abilities. But I don't understand. How is it the doctor was killed, when normally he would have been with the headquarters facility and therefore not directly in the midst of a battle?"

"Normally it would be as you say, but in this case the battle spread rapidly over a large area, and the headquarters facility was overrun and almost totally destroyed. As you know, at this point in time, the war is no longer confined to guerrilla warfare, but waged by large units engaging in intense battles. This is evidenced by the fact that in recent months eight army doctors have been killed."

Our talk about the young woman, Phuong Nghi, made me think of Như Nguyện, my young woman. My heart sank. At one of the recent press receptions, when mentioning the trip to Geneva of the minister of foreign affairs, one of my colleagues unintentionally asked no one in particular whether Như Nguyện had gone with the delegation as the irreplaceable private secretary of the minister. Though not knowing how much truth there was in his snide remark, what I heard brought doubt and pain.

"By the way, I haven't seen Như Nguyện around for quite a while," Davis said. "I want to invite the two of you to dinner at Kyo, an authentic Japanese restaurant which has just opened.

Certainly Như Nguyện knows Japanese food better than you and I."

"Như Nguyện has just left for Geneva, I don't know for how long. If it's convenient, perhaps instead I can bring along your possible assistant, Phuong Nghi."

Davis and I agreed on a dinner date at Kyo Restaurant. I left his paper's offices and moved toward the elevator, the unfounded rumor about Như Nguyện haunting me to no end.

CHAPTER NINE

"This is my last night in Vietnam," General Hunting told the two of us, Davis and I.

"What?" I exclaimed. "Has your tour of duty already terminated here? Why do you leave, when the Thuong people and the highlands still need you?"

"It's not my wish to abandon them; nothing like that. After more than a year here, it's time I return to America."

"I hope to see you again."

"Oh, no," he protested. "I want to return to Vietnam as a country in peace."

I laughed and told the general that I would like to see him come back as a tourist. Hunting said he was very sad to leave Vietnam. During his several-decades-long military career, he had been posted in many countries, but had never felt attached to any of them the way he had been to this country, a devastated and exhausted land whose brave and courageous people still fought to protect it. In the presence of friends like Davis and myself, these words from the mouth of a military officer seemed sincere, devoid of diplomatic pretension. In contrast to Davis's slim and fragile physical appearance, the general was big, his face wide and heavy, his voice strong.

I continued. "Upon hearing that all of a sudden you are being transferred to another post, the Thuong people expressed their regret that they will no longer be seeing their benefactor. Nay Ry, a Thuong intellectual has, with fear, predicted that some unfortunate thing will happen in the highlands. Is there something out of the ordinary in your return to America? Nay Ry said that you were posted in An Khe for only a little over a year."

"Such a short period has been enough to take a great slice out of my life," Hunting replied. "There's nothing out of the ordinary in my military life; there is only discipline and orders from above. My only regret is that I have to abandon the civil operations programs we have begun, programs which, among other things, send army doctors deep into mountainous villages to treat illnesses and distribute medicines to ethnic tribes. I am not sure the programs will be continued as we wish."

Though he did not delineate the difficulties, I could well appreciate the various internal problems the general had had to confront: from the brazen-faced Tacelosky to the undisciplined Green Beret units who fought valiantly like mercenaries, and, on a higher level, I could not but think of Dr. Ross.

As usual, Davis assumed the humorous tone of voice typical of Asia when he joined in. "Can you think of any other American general besides General Hunting who received in one tour of duty an American Silver Star, a National Order Medal which is given by the Vietnamese government to foreigners who have rendered great service to Vietnam, plus a National Gold Medal from the president of Korea, an award to honor foreigners who have contributed to the welfare of his country. The general's return to

America to work at the Pentagon can be seen as a promotion in the same way that Westy, General Westmoreland, was promoted."

General Hunting smiled rather bitterly. "A veteran combat general assigned to a desk is no different than a retired general. There's no comfort in it. While in the highlands, I was so busy and so tired that I did not have time to think about anything. But now that I am in Saigon doing nothing but awaiting my return to America, the thought has occurred to me that after all, I am already over fifty. Davis, isn't it amazing that it has been twenty-five years since the Second World War when we got to know each other as neighbors, when you were still a teenager going to the same high school I had attended? Let's drink to our twenty-five-year-old friendship. And you too, our reporter, won't you join us?"

While gulping down a glass of wine, I suddenly thought of the image which the celebrated writer Nhất Linh had mockingly applied to himself when he left *Suối Đa Mê*, "Stream of Many Passions" in Dalat, to run a journal in Saigon. The image was that of an old elephant in a zoo, an image that could equally well be applied to General Hunting when installed at the Pentagon in Washington.

Abruptly, the general returned to the question of the highlands in addressing both Davis and myself. "Do you think the Kinh-Thuong conflict is so serious as to be described as beyond conciliation and mediation, which is the point of view of a number of Americans like Tacelosky?"

A reply from my position as a Kinh person might not be considered an objective assessment, so I deferred it to Davis.

"The conflict is there, no doubt about it, but it's not a clear black-and-white picture; it's somewhere in the gray area," Davis began. "There is absolutely no racial discrimination in the proper sense of the term, like the way the Germans treated the Jews, like the hatred between blacks and whites in America. This is evidenced by the fact that in the history of Vietnam there has never been a campaign of genocide like Hitler's extermination of the Jews, or a movement in the nature of the KKK in America. What's wonderful is the ease with which multiple ethnic groups and various religions have coexisted for several thousand years on this continent. The synthesis in Vietnam of three religions— Buddhism, Taoism, and Confucianism—is eloquent proof of that.

"In my opinion, the fundamental cause of the drawn-out tragedy in the highlands did not originate from racial conflict, but from inequality between Kinh and Thuong in terms of rights and opportunities for advancement. The point worth noting is that, given the abject poverty of the Thuong, the inequality is much sharper than a mere discrepancy between poverty in rural areas and the material comfort available in cities. In any event, both of these cases of disparity demand a suitable solution, which is no less than a revolution for social justice. The ongoing war will, as a matter of course, die out gradually when the very reason for it ceases to exist."

I was astounded that Davis could come up with such a calm and clear assessment of the situation, which obviously required an extensive knowledge of Asia. I was certain that no other American had similar ideas.

By way of describing the complex nature of the coexistence of so many ethnic groups in Vietnam, I related to the general and Davis the myth of the birth of one hundred clans from a hundred eggs. The story is centered around the marriage, in a remote mythical past, between Lady Âu Cơ, a fairy from the mountains, and Lạc Long Quân, a dragon king from the sea. Lady Âu Cơ gave birth to a pouch containing a hundred eggs, from which emerged a hundred sons. These sons of a fairy-and-dragon match were the ancestors of *Bách Việt*, the hundred Viet clans, who continued their existence in this land until the present day.

I concluded. "The people of Vietnam live in their predestined land, haunted by the historical threat of a southward expansion and annexation by China. Because of that common fear, they conduct their lives in relative harmony and unity, sharing a history of over four thousand years."

Davis further elaborated my view to Hunting. "And what's remarkable is that out of those four thousand years, they survived more than a thousand years of Chinese domination without being assimilated, which fact kept intact the territory and culture of Vietnam as we know it today. Against the obvious edification provided by such a historical lesson, I believe that many, including a number of Americans, made a mistake when they exploited small conflicts in the hope of creating a historic separation in this weakening nation. We Americans have come here to resolve a war, but at the same time we ourselves are sowing the seeds of another war. It's about time we put an end to that delusory undertaking."

Seemingly uninformed of secret factors behind political troubles in the highlands, the general voiced his puzzlement. "But there must be some sound reason for Americans to engage in such an action. As I understand it, in the years before 1954, the Central Highlands were the place where communist guerrillas for a long time set up ambushes, and this mountainous region was also a bloody battlefield upon which many allied French-Vietnamese troops died.

"Since the beginning of this present war, the highlands have been the primary concern of the American military. More than sixty fortified SFOBs were built for no other purpose than to control the highlands as a springboard from which to lock out all possible infiltration from the border areas. One must admit that due credit should be given to the first Green Berets from Fort Bragg who established the first effective system of defense in the highlands. And I am told that up until now, their relationship with the Thuong has been good and warm. It's also worth noting that the Green Berets have been quite successful, not only in Vietnam, but also with many half-civilized ethnic groups in other countries."

Davis displayed a half smile, the smile of one who knew too much and comprehended many things and their deepest secrets. He said, "Right. They were trained to engage in unconventional warfare, but I don't think that is sufficient reason for them to support a naive movement to turn the Central Highlands into one more state of the United States. You have to be completely ignorant about Asia to believe in such a silly scheme. While President Kennedy enlarged the number of Green Berets in the wish that they become valiant fighters for freedom and liberation, almost all the countries where they have been did not quite accept their presence and looked at them as saboteurs and experts in overthrowing governments."

It seemed that Davis was the only American very much dissatisfied with the role of the United States in the Vietnam War. The heated discussion was growing rather tense, not suitable for the occasion—which was meant by the general to be a farewell dinner. In an attempt to lighten the atmosphere, I joked that if it was true that America had been so involved in so many different things that whatever good or bad occurrence that transpired in Vietnam could be attributed to the work of the CIA, then America was quite a superpower and both the general and Davis should be proud of it.

Davis did not share my humor. "That fact," he said, "is actually damaging to the reputation of America, and it is our power that will isolate us from the rest of the word. Returning to the case of Vietnam, and specifically the highlands matter, I have written so many times expressing the idea that it's time Washington make a clear-cut choice between their illusory short-term interests and viable relations with their allies. No matter how much the State Department attempts to explain away, everyone knows that Washington has provided support, secretly if not officially, or has intentionally looked the other way, as a number of Americans have overtly trampled upon the sovereignty of this nation, even as they fight side-by-side with the South Vietnamese against the communists.

"When back there in Washington, using your position, you must inform the leadership that even when engaging in an unconventional war America cannot abandon basic agreements made with their allies. There's not much time left before we enter the twenty-first century, a time long past the golden colonial period so enjoyed by the white man. The Pacific Ocean is there to put a stop to the inexhaustible westward movement of some Americans."

Abruptly Davis stopped, apparently sensing the tension caused by his argument. He then lowered his voice and calmly continued. "We are in a period that witnesses great leaps in conquering outer space, with a plan to land men on the moon, and we must live up to the demands of the times."

Davis's thought appeared to have made a deep impression on the general. Among close friends, Davis shed his normal reserve and enthusiastically expressed himself. "Contemporary history of Vietnam," continued Davis, "has more than once proved this point: a Cochinchina belonging to France, and cut off completely from the territory of Vietnam, was an impossible dream of the French, as it went against the wishes of the Vietnamese themselves who inhabited that part of the country. This was so even though at that time the French government in Paris supported the policy of acquiring colonies, and the anticolonial movement worldwide had not yet begun to hinder their design.

"Like the French, what the Americans intend to do in the highlands will not go anywhere; rather, the result will only leave an ugly mark in the history of relations between Vietnam and the U.S., presenting nothing but bitter experience for other allies to contemplate. Even granted that fighting communism is our ultimate aim, that aim cannot justify the means we are using here.

"I also don't believe that more than sixty SFOBs, no matter how solid and strong, are capable of tightly closing the border to outsiders. Otherwise, fierce battles would not have been waged during the last rainy season, during which encounters you yourself had to fight so hard. In my view, it is the Kinh-Thuong conflict that is being exploited, weakening the defense system of the highlands, and in the end only the enemy benefits from it all."

Laughing gently, the general commented. "It's no wonder that a number of Americans consider you Asianized. Is that a correct description, Davis?"

"Just like you, Hunting. You are thought to be too humane with regard to tactics in a war that has turned unconventional. And I ask myself whether humaneness or humanity is something we should be ashamed of."

Changing the subject, the general asked Davis when he would be transferred to the Paris bureau.

"You know," Davis replied, "just like you, I don't feel like leaving Vietnam, even for Paris, an assignment desired by many."

Davis went on to remark that if no big changes came to his life, he would remain here indefinitely, living in the vicissitudes of Southeast Asia. He asserted that the difficult years spent in Asia were a string of happy days to him.

Hunting laughed. "Your happiness will be complete if and when you marry a very pretty Asian woman. My wife Marcolina always wonders when you will say good-bye to the bachelor's life."

As usual, Davis grew embarrassed and rather ill at ease at the mention of women. I thought of Phuong Nghi and a possible turning point in his future.

Hunting addressed Davis. "The painting that you send along will be treasured by Marcolina. She is very keen on art, and I am sure she will love it."

It was my painting entitled "Serenity" he was talking about. It was responsible for the start of the relationship between Davis and myself. Hunting expressed pleasure upon learning that I was the creator of the painting, and he was very surprised when told that I had stopped painting to enter journalism.

"Tell Marcolina," said Davis, "that I am sending her the painting with a lot of cherished memories behind it. And I particularly thank her for the care she gives my lonely old mother back there."

Davis also asked Hunting the favor of delivering two new cassette tapes, which served as a means of communication between him and his mother. I promised Davis that when in Hue, if I could paint again, I would send him another painting to cover the empty stretch of his wall. Hunting teasingly said that if he ever returned to Vietnam as a tourist, along with his wife, he hoped he would be able to visit me at an art studio, rather than at a newspaper's office.

CHAPTER TEN

I had not imagined that Như Nguyện's trip abroad could have left me with the joyless days I was now experiencing. Indeed, other than hours busy with work, I spent the rest of my days in a dark mood of longing.

This morning, the newspaper's office looked deserted. As soon as he saw my face, the editor began to nag. Even though I appreciated the agony he suffered, stemming from the fact that his son, having just graduated from a college in France, decided to go to Hanoi instead of returning to Saigon, I could not help being annoyed. That the printing house was experiencing electricity failure added to his foul mood, which he took out on anyone who happened to be in his path. My cool and forgiving response seemed to provoke him, for he talked to me in an irritated tone of voice.

"Where have you disappeared to for almost a week now?" he asked. "For what did you go up to the highlands so often? Why was it so necessary for you to attend that conference on the

Thuong matter? You have to make a choice, being an anthropologist or a journalist."

He had never talked to me in quite that way before. Silently, I walked toward the window and looked down upon traffic flows lining the roadway below. Swarming ants. On the other side of the street, a sentinel of oil drums painted white and filled with cement surrounded the entrance to a high-rise building complex where only Americans were seen. I still derived pleasure from being a journalist under the present circumstances, and had not definitely made up my mind on another choice. The agreement to teach at the College of Fine Arts in Hue was made more on impulse than on serious consideration. Acting as though there was no reason to think of destiny, I felt I could freely chart my future.

Only when the editor's face appeared calmer did I try to start a conversation. I asked him about a press delegation that had been invited to visit Korea.

He remembered it, and immediately said to me, "Your time would be better spent on that kind of trip. If you want, I will suggest that you be included in the group. The Koreans' ten-year-long experience in rebuilding their country after a destructive war is something we should examine and learn from. The Vietnam War will end some time. Preparing ourselves to receive peace while the country is at war is an intelligent and necessary attitude."

Since he always treated me with kindness and sincerity, no matter what he said, I knew he would not prevent me from going to the highlands again. For this reason, I could not terminate my service with his small paper in order to work with Davis.

From a drawer, the editor extracted a big envelope and handed it to me. "Two days ago a lieutenant colonel came to look for you. He left this package and said that it was a gift sent to you by General Thuyet before he went back to I Corps after a short visit in Saigon. How come you seem so close to the general?"

"We are not exactly close. I have met and had meals with the general a few times, that's all. His deep warm feelings, if any, are due to the reputation and prestige of our paper."

The editor appeared moved by my heartfelt comments.

In the envelope were specially printed copies of two booklets of essays by General Thuyet which had just been published, and a very nice portrait photo of the general himself, in color, complete with his autograph. I smiled inwardly. It was common knowledge among the literary circle that the general's entourage included an advisory group, among whom were a couple of ghostwriters who helped him turn into a published author. These two works undoubtedly constituted an effort to promote the image of this rather controversial officer.

The first work, *Victory in the Rainy Season*, dealing with large battles fought and won in the Central Highlands, was meant to show the general as a Young Turk endowed with excellent combat skills. The second, *Thoughts on the Two Revolutions*, was obviously a clever borrowing from the title of the book by President Nasser of Egypt, *The Philosophy of the Revolution* published in 1959, which had a great impact on the Young Turks, the powerful elite of the military forces of South Vietnam after the 1963 Revolution had put an end to the government of President Diem. By this intentional borrowing, the general's advisory group seemed to entertain the thought of elevating him to the level of the dynamic Egyptian leader. Just as Nasser talked about social and agricultural reform as the main reason behind the 1952 revolution that toppled King Farouk and which was led by Nasser himself, a colonel at the time, General Thuyet's essay focused on his thoughts on the social revolution South Vietnam sorely needed. The work was thus designed to highlight the general's potential as a politician.

When I showed the booklets to him, the editor expressed surprise. "Hmmm, I didn't know the general also writes books. I have never heard about that."

A glance at the first few lines of one of the works was enough to tell me that it was the typically oratorical and bewitchingly persuasive language of the writer who was the principal advisor to the general. Like many other authors who had moved south when Vietnam was temporarily divided in 1954, this writer had expected to enjoy a freedom of expression that the communist north would not allow. The authoritarian rule of President Diem's family, with its absolutely strict censorship, crushed that hope, making him pessimistic and despondent. Then the 1963 Revolution liberated his pen, and now he was free to wield it under the wing of the general.

I offered the booklets to the editor. "I will leave them here for you to read first. It appears that the general has plenty of goodwill toward the press, so I don't really understand why American journalists resent and detest him so much. I have not seen any article by Americans on Vietnamese military leadership that includes positive comments about him. This is so much the case that I have the impression there is a campaign by the Western press to smear his name, particularly with regard to matters connected with his tough policy in the highlands."

I told the editor that during one of my trips to Pleiku, General Thuyet had sent me as a present a rather large sum of money, which I had a difficult time declining. The general had said that it was no more than his habitual gesture of goodwill toward all journalists covering news in the highlands.

"I still think journalistic independence is possible only when supported by financial independence," I continued. "I want to be free in expressing my true judgment and evaluation of the general, voicing criticism and praises wherever they are due, so that in any situation I won't feel that I am not playing fair with him."

The editor leaned back in his chair, pushed down the frame of his glasses against the bridge of his nose, and spoke in a gentle, soft voice. "I completely agree with your independent attitude. I have never regretted placing so much trust in you. With more than forty years in journalism, I am proud to have kept myself clean to this day. Right now, temptations abound. People have promised to contribute a lot of money to expand the paper, money said to be without strings attached. But I have firmly refused their offers."

The editor's experience and position on money matters proved the contrary to the statement that the writer-advisor to the general had expressed at one time: that making a living in Vietnamese journalism in the long run would necessarily force one to become a hack writer or likely a bitter soul. After many ups and downs, the editor remained a person holding to many conservative ideals. But no matter how much he was pleased with my work, he still found at least one weakness to criticize, one constraint upon my ability to successfully function as a liberal journalist.

"The only problem is, you are too much of an artist," he continued. "It is not that I don't like it. I only want to say that once you have chosen a career in journalism, you must accept its discipline, and only when you have adapted yourself to it do you have the potential of becoming very good in your work."

In the editor's view, what was potentially good about my ability was always to be seen in the future, in just the manner that a great book imagined to be in the making is always formed by lines as yet to be written. And just as in my painting career a great work was always in the process of being created! I smiled, staring at his lethargic gait as he walked away, a gait like that of an old monk. How secretly tickled I was with that comparison!

After he had left, I began my routine work. Among a pile of mail from readers that lay in disarray, I recognized a letter from Takashi with French stamps on it. We had known each other a few years back when Takashi Oka was posted to Saigon as a reporter for the *Christian Science Monitor*. We had at that time often exchanged news and discussed political events. Since he had been transferred to become the bureau chief in Paris, he had not neglected to send me a postcard now and then, expressing the usual niceties and stating his hope of keeping our friendship intact. This gesture of unconditional loyalty and warmth could only be expected from an Asian, especially from a Japanese, I thought.

The rest of the mail was to be sorted out by the secretary. The office also received plenty of books and newspapers, which I had no time to read properly and seriously. The five-hundred-page book written by Do, the cover of which I designed, came with a truly flattering line of dedication: "This is the book most favored by its author for its beautiful appearance."

What caught my attention was a special issue of the student association's paper focusing on Vietnamese sovereignty in the Central Highlands. The appraisals expressed were bold and extremist in nature, even as they exhibited the purity of the students' thoughts. The major theme that the highlands was being pulled every which way was presented by a political cartoon featuring a horse cart with three drivers upon it, each facing and pointing his finger in a different direction. The drivers wore three different hats with three little flags of America, Hanoi, and Saigon attached to them. The U.S. side was most strongly attacked and disparaged by the student writers. Nor was General Thuyet able to escape their attack, which was a pity. So it turned out that two of the three mutual enemies could well equally be considered the opposition by a removed third party, in this case the students, a third party whose only power was the power of resistance.

I had the intention of meeting and talking with these amateur journalists. They might provide me with numerous new ideas, one of which I had already picked up: their suggestion that a

Department of Anthropology be established as part of the University of Saigon to support research done by the Department of Highlands Affairs. Only these young students could be hoped to bring new vitality to the highlands. Once again, I saw that General Thuyet had had good reason in this case for wanting to invest in the younger generation.

My watch said it was 6 o'clock, the usual time of day I turned on the radio to catch the brief evening news report from the U.S. Army station. Perhaps my watch was running a couple of minutes ahead of time, as when the machine was flipped on only a piece of music in between programs could be heard. It was a familiar piece, every note of which was a fervid kiss triggering memories of the first days I lived with Như Nguyện. Those were days I truly lived my life contentedly beside a woman. I did not have any plan for the future, but I thought perhaps Như Nguyện was the woman I could marry. Given my lifestyle at present, a traditional wife, gentle and well-behaved, was out of the question.

The first item of the short five-minute-news bulletin jolted me with an electrical surge. In despair, I heard the shocking news that the communists had attacked the Thuong refugees from Dakto village who had been safely installed in a resettlement center. Almost six hundred villagers had been killed, an event labeled by the American radio station in Saigon as "Vietnam vengeance." It was no doubt the highest number of civilian casualties in a single incident recorded since the war transited from guerrilla warfare into regular warfare.

Turning off the radio, I drove in haste to Davis's newspaper's office. It was closed. Returning to my office, I found it deserted save for the secretary still working at some last task of the day. I placed many telephone calls to various places with the hope of locating Davis, but without success. The only thing I could do was to show up for my dinner date with him at *Cercle Sportif,* the sports club inherited from the French.

I was early for the appointment. People were still at their match on the tennis court. A beautiful woman sat among a group of children playing in the water of the pool, her dreamy eyes full of joy. I casually looked around and was annoyed to see Tacelosky sporting his thin mustache in the company of another Asian woman. Though his special mission concerned highlands affairs, he was seen in Saigon very often. His thick face, forever nonchalant beside a glass of alcohol and in the smoke of a cigarette, made me wonder about his work habits. Tacelosky recognized me immediately. When I related the news of the massacre, his face remained cold, betraying no emotion.

"Did that really happen?" he asked, making display of his usual nonchalance. "Perhaps the journalist Davis knows about it better than I. Why don't you seek him out?"

Politely, he pulled up a chair for me. "Would you like cognac and soda?"

I had to admire his superior memory. We had met only once, but he remembered even such an unimportant habit of mine. Being a member of the press, I had learned to tolerate all sorts of people I talked with, even when they did not like me much. I said my thanks and sat down. In no time at all, Tacelosky brought up the name of General Thuyet. I realized that it was not merely a casual mention for the sake of conversation when he mockingly remarked, "I didn't know that in your democratic society, there still live among you some mandarins of the Nguyen dynasty."

I simply smiled as if agreeing and appreciating his apt comparison, while my inner self was anxiously waiting for Davis's arrival. In the end, Davis did not show up for the dinner appointment, which was something he rarely did. I drove to his office and saw him in a state of agony.

In a voice choked with emotion and tears, Davis said, "You couldn't find a single person among more than six hundred Thuong villagers who survived intact, unmaimed. That was a most savage act of vengeance. Not being able to draw the refugees to their side, the communists mobilized their forces to destroy the resettlement center. They even used flamethrowers to burn women and children who hid themselves in underground shelters. The whole place was reduced to piles of burned wood and hundreds of corpses."

I voiced my puzzlement about the government's role in the protection of the center.

"As you know," Davis speculated, "in theory, depending on the territorial divisions of the highlands, security is entrusted to either the Vietnamese or the Americans. This particular resettlement center was located in a division for which an American Special Forces camp was responsible. The communists could in no way penetrate such a fortified location. But they did. Given the ongoing conflict between the American Special Forces and the Saigon government, perhaps this was one of Tacelosky's schemes: practice nonintervention, leaving it to General Tri and the ARVN to protect the very Thuong group they had previously rescued from the communists. This could be a very good way to prove the incompetency of the ARVN in the eyes of Thuong resistance fighters. If that was the actual scenario, it was most barbaric."

Tacelosky would definitely be one who could act like that, I thought. He was capable of sacrificing six hundred lives just to prove a point: security and happiness of the Thuong people can only be effectively guaranteed by the American Green Berets.

Not being able to control himself, Davis wept when showing me photos of the devastated resettlement center and piles of dead bodies. There was a photo of a mother holding her baby, both charred by flamethrowers.

Suddenly Davis's room turned cold. The crossbow and arrows were no more than dark marks on the white wall, a painful memory evoking the tragic lives of the six hundred. My eyes sought respite in pausing upon the blue and white sections of a big map spread across the coffee table. I saw nothing but blotches of color.

On his typewriter, Davis had written his first lines describing the tragedy: *The dream of the Thuong people to survive is being crushed by the barbaric forms of vengeance employed by all sides involved in the war in the highlands.* He then posed the ultimate question: *What do the responsible people expect the world to think of this bloody massacre?*

This question had to be answered by people like General Thuyet and Tacelosky, as well as by FULRO. I myself was professionally interested primarily in recording facts and events, and for that reason I planned to go back to the highlands the next day to dig deeper into the last hours of the tragedy.

CHAPTER ELEVEN

What do they expect the world to think of this?

The whole planet answered Davis's question with shock, extreme anger, and indignation. The foreign press uniformly called it a "Vietnamese way of vengeance." In the highlands, the days immediately after the massacre were the most traumatic, a time of loss and grief experienced by the Thuong minorities who lived in perpetual darkness and whose only hope was to survive. The Thuong separatist movement took full advantage of the tragedy, using it as a just cause for agitation. Even the conciliatory and moderate intellectuals, Y Ksor and Nay Ry, attempted to mobilize their people to sign a petition to the government, the essential message of which was their demand to have the right to live and be protected in their own lands. As to the American Special Forces, the loss of six hundred lives was regarded a triumphant confirmation of their superiority vis-à-vis the ARVN. These soldiers found staunch support from the Thuong Civil Irregular Defense Groups and by the whole lot of their interpreters. Nay Ry compared the mass of Thuong people to a square piece of cloth, each corner being yanked and pulled vigorously by one side in the conflict toward its field of influence.

When I arrived, two days after the event, the resettlement center was still very much a battleground soaked in the strong smell of death. All was burned to ashes, save for twisted sheets of corrugated metal. Even though the corpses, or what was left of them, had been collected and buried in a mass grave, the fetid smell still lingered in the air. A scene parallel to that of Picasso's *Guernica* appeared before my awareness, but one with fierce and sorrowful colors. On banners of coarse white cotton flown on poles driven into the ground were painted words in lines of gaudy red, words with their English translations condemning the communists and calling for Kinh-Thuong unity in a spirit of common progress. People looked for significant echo from the mass grave.

"You may be interested to know," said the Vietnamese captain who had guided me to the resettlement location, "that during the same night this transpired, a group of Thuong separatists stealthily found their way here and hung the tricolor flag of their proclaimed autonomous homeland *Dega*. They scattered propaganda leaflets accusing the communists and the Saigon government of being accomplices in plotting to annihilate the Thuong ethnic minorities. They also requested that America re-examine its policy of aid to Vietnam. Further, they even called for intervention by the UN through Phnom Penh, which they proclaimed would be strongly backed by the Congress of Indochinese Ethnic Groups, an organization set up by the French."

The captain had the strong heavy face of a military person. He spoke the dialect of Bui Chu, a predominantly Catholic area of North Vietnam, and was likely an extremist Christian. He handed me some leaflets.

"See for yourself, Mr. Reporter," he demanded, handing over a sample. "Judging from the quality of the paper and the printing technique, one cannot help but reach the obvious conclusion regarding its origin. Right smack dab from the helping hands of the USIS!"

The captain's observation was not unreasonable when one considered that the Thuong, living in isolation in the jungles, forever threatened and hunted, still managed to establish contact with the outside world and conduct their activities by use of modern technology.

"Do you know, Mr. Reporter," he continued in vexation, his thick eyebrows drawn together, "that the Thuong asked the Americans for help to chase the Vietnamese out of the highlands, so they could establish an autonomous nation under American protection? In my opinion, we will eventually take control of the situation and then all the troubles in the highlands will disappear. This won't be difficult to accomplish given that the Thuong are of such small numbers and scattered over the mountains."

I was not sure how to measure the extent of ruthlessness in the captain's statement, but it brought to mind the strange idea expressed by American military officers.

"Captain," I said, "to solve the problem is not the same as to outright kill it. I am afraid that advocacy of such drastic measures sounds no less bizarre than the declaration by American military officers that they could easily beat the communists in Vietnam if they had not to contend with Vietnamese allies."

The captain's face fell, and he kept silent. Obviously, he was not pleased with my expressed point of view. He declined to continue the conversation. This was all the better, as aside from the need of transportation provided by him, I was also in need of silence for contemplation. I expressed my wish to visit other resettlement camps besides this place of tragedy. The present event had proven once again that history forever consisted of repetitions. Many more lives would be sacrificed, given that each side wanted to yank and tear a bigger fragment of the cloth for itself.

Contrary to the temperament of the typical military man, who by discipline had few words, the captain could not stay silent for long and was ever ready with his verbal expressions.

"I do not agree," he began again, "with General Tri's current policy of entrusting to the Americans the distribution of relief to the Thuong people—even when the Americans are Minister and Mrs. Denman. The barbaric savages are grateful and obedient only to those who press food into their mouths. Therefore, it is not without reason that the Americans have tried to monopolize relief operations—even back during the time of General Thuyet. I myself quite agree with the unequivocal standpoint maintained by General Thuyet."

Once again I was made aware that General Thuyet by his firm policy had left his mark and influence in the highlands. For certain, the massacre must have evoked in him strong reactions and even indignant anger. Situated in Da Nang-Hue area, the general still considered the highlands his second home, a place to which he was bound by many spiritual responsibilities. Indeed, during the various times of trouble in the past, he had always provided moral support to his subordinates. These loyal onetime subordinates continued to believe that it would not be long before General Thuyet returned to the highlands.

"Mr. Reporter," the captain continued, "have you heard anything about the news that General Tri is about to be promoted to the rank of lieutenant general?"

"Yes, I have heard something to that effect. On this coming national day, quite a few generals will earn another star. But I did not hear the name of General Thuyet among those mentioned."

The captain's lack of enthusiasm for General Tri was clearly revealed in what he decided to confide in me.

"You know," he said, "sometimes promotion is part of a smooth transition in an officer's departure for some other place.

In my view, General Tri is not of a high enough caliber to deal with both the communists and the Americans. As an officer of lower rank, when witnessing the way Tacelosky behaved toward General Tri, I myself felt ashamed and sorry for the general. Let me ask you something: What the hell is this American other than a lieutenant colonel retired from Special Forces now representing USAID in the highlands? Is he CIA? Even if so, why does the general seem afraid of him?"

I myself certainly knew why the general was intimidated by Tacelosky. Having lost control of his wife, the general had gone deep into many dirty businesses, everything from appropriation of others' land to corrupt practices in the development of An Khe. Knowledge of all that was the trump card that Tacelosky held, which conveniently allowed him to blackmail the general any time he chose. As a result, the general's policy was to practice smooth conciliation and tolerance until the time he could leave his post peacefully.

The deeper he got into conversation with me, the more clearly the captain showed himself to be a perpetually dissatisfied person.

"I'd like to tell you something else," he said in a confidential tone of voice. "You know that I am a Catholic refugee from the North, very keen on anticommunism and, therefore, willing to agree to the American presence. However, I did not expect that in the middle of the twentieth century there still exist blatant American colonialists like Tacelosky. The presence of people like that spoils the good intentions behind the American assistance and aid programs."

I had been told that the captain was a stubborn individual who, like the majority of other officers transferred to the highlands, had been sent there as a form of exile. It was clear that he still held many illusions about the selfless goodness of the

Americans. I asked him what he thought about the role of Denman and his wife. The captain's eyebrows drew together in a fierce manner.

"No place in the highlands has been spared their footsteps," he answered. "It was thanks to them that American Special Forces were able to build their camps in mountainous villages. Though I am a genuine Christian, deep in my heart I do not believe in the almost purely social agenda of Christian missionaries. From the point of view of one who knows how to draw valuable lessons from history, I cannot help but come to that realization."

I was rather surprised that the captain could articulate so well. He also told me of the direct influence the minister and his wife exerted on Tacelosky.

"In my own view," he concluded, "Tacelosky, Minister Denman, and General Hunting represent different ways of doing things by the Americans—all directed toward one goal. Sometimes I feel that the goal lies beyond all the facts I know. The more I consider it, the more contradictions I find."

Talking about contradictions, I was shown one such in the manner by which the Thuong around me responded to the dregs of Western civilization. Mountain girls awkwardly wore sandals, while some Thuong men donned skirts. The person who took me on a tour of his village was an elderly man who walked barefoot and had solemnly put on a jacket to go with his traditional loincloth. The different pieces of clothing they wore were castoffs, euphemistically called gifts from the American people to friends in the free world.

I then ran into Denman and his wife, through whom my conversations with the Thuong became easier. I intended to use the remainder of the morning on a photojournalism project focused on the mountainous villages I visited.

"Minister," I jokingly said to Denman, "the man in the red skirt over there presents a strange, unusual image. And for a journalist, he can become a news item."

At other times, perhaps, the minister would have laughed and appreciated my humor. But today his face remained quite serious, his eyes reflecting still the devastating pain experienced from the tragedy. Like a professor of psychology, he formulated a psychological reading.

"As you may imagine," he said gravely, "these days the Thuong tribes live their lives in utter confusion and fear. It's extreme fear that usually leads to unimaginably violent acts. You know that to them both the communists and the southern nationalists are all Vietnamese, and even though the crime was committed by the communist side, we ourselves must bear the consequences. I am afraid that one day they will suddenly rise up all over the highlands. No one can predict to what extent massacres will be perpetrated on both sides in this conflict."

I noted the minister's clever way with words when he included himself in the inclusive "we," here alluding to Vietnamese. Had I not known his true intent, I would have easily shared his point of view. I kept quiet and listened to what he next had to say.

"In my view, as the saying goes, sooner or later what belongs to Caesar must be returned to Caesar. That requires wisdom and clear-sightedness from both Vietnamese highlanders and lowlanders—and from the Americans too. People like General Thuyet and Tacelosky are not gentle hands that effectively soothe the wounds of the highlands . . . By the way, what do think of General Tri? He seems a rather amicable person, don't you think?"

To praise a general for his amicability was no less than to show reservations about his military abilities. I was sure Denman knew better than anybody else that General Tri was weak and could be directly manipulated by himself, who would be the natural choice of a mediator in any negotiations between the two opposing sides.

After the event of the massacre, a big unit of the First Air Cavalry Division was posted near the headquarters facility across from the military hospital. Streams of helicopters and tanks, one after another entering the area, lifted and spread red dust through the air, choking carpets of green grass when it settled.

The few surviving Thuong persons were all injured to one or another degree, mostly suffering from shrapnel wounds caused by grenades. A doctor led Denman and I to the bed of a mother and child. The mother was still deep in a coma.

"The mother was very seriously burned," the doctor told us. "Actually, her entire back was burned, while the child was unharmed. I suppose that at the point of danger, the mother used her back as a shield to protect her child from a flame thrower."

With respect to the mother's critical condition, the doctor was very pessimistic.

"Over 50 percent of her burns are of the third degree. There's no hope she will survive until tomorrow," he said.

Except for the child who was four years old, the whole family was killed. The minister expressed his wish to take care of the child.

"I will entrust the little girl to my wife, who can nurse her to health. Then I will send her to the journalist Davis. Davis often says he wishes to adopt a child like this."

I knew that Davis had sponsored a blind child he had found wandering alone in an isolated mountainous village. Now, the child lived in comfort with young friends of his in Australia.

In my career as a journalist, this was the first time I used my camera to capture images of such horrible destruction to the human body as those of the woman victim.

At the invitation of the minister, I visited his home for the second time, the first being in Davis's company. The current con-

flict between American Special Forces and the Saigon government had so much jeopardized the security situation that Dr. and
Mrs. Denman no longer lived in the Rhadé village as before.
They had moved all their modern household effects to the town
center of Pleiku, and sent their daughter back to America for her
education.

"We moved not simply because of anxiety over lack of security, as having lived here for many years, my wife and I are used
to such a tense atmosphere," the minister explained. "The main
issue has to do with the matter of delivering relief to new Thuong
hamlets. The number of these hamlets is increasing steadily,
which makes the hard job even more difficult, and I don't want to
disappoint the General. I am sure you know my happiness now is
identical to that of the Thuong people, and the Central Highlands
can be said to be my second homeland."

General Thuyet, Minister Denman, and perhaps even
Tacelosky all wanted to consider the wild highlands their homeland. That desire to monopolize this mountainous part of the
country was the root cause of conflict, I reflected.

The new home of the Denmans, located next to the former
Emperor Bảo Đại's Royal Summer Palace, surrounded by a garden of deep green trees, was larger and much more beautiful than
their previous residence. Stepping into the living room, I discovered that Denman was an amateur painter. An easel, a stretched
canvas, a palette, palette knives, and paintbrushes were neatly
arranged, perhaps by the tender hand of Mrs. Denman. What was
missing, perhaps, was the carefree air of creative disorder typically associated with an artist's world.

"I heard from Davis that you are a talented painter. Is that
right?" Denman asked. "I myself had only a single occasion to
view your paintings, when I paid a visit once to Davis's newspaper's office. To me, the most happy life, perhaps, is that of a
genuine artist."

I had no thought to offer, so I only smiled in reply.

On the canvas sitting upon the easel was an unfinished painting of a strong and healthy Thuong young woman, half-naked, busying herself with a few slats of bamboo in the process of weaving. The bright colors were still freshly wet. I was rather surprised to observe that the nakedness of the woman—which through Denman's religious vision should have been as natural as the air she breathed—was in fact awash with a sense of sexuality. I looked for an explanation in the idea of a sexually repressed ecclesiastic. The minister seemed anxiously, rather awkwardly, awaiting my comments.

Tapping the bowl of his pipe against a ceramic ashtray, he said in a defensive tone, "I have just learned to paint, and realize that painting is an enjoyable entertainment. A writer yourself, I am sure you appreciate that sometimes it's virtually impossible to write anything, for example during the time of grief and tension these last few days."

Seeing that I had not much enthusiasm for the subject of painting, Denman adroitly switched to another topic. "Relative to painting, when talking about colors, one thinks at once of harmony," he redirected his line of thought. "Harmony is also a necessary ingredient of our lives, and it is equally so in the Kinh-Thuong relationship, as I see it. We must, accordingly, consider the matter of face-saving and suitable methods of reconciliation acceptable to both sides. To establish an independent *Dega* nation is a utopian plan on the part of the separatist movement, whereas the Vietnamese intention to eliminate the ethnic minorities, with their unique cultures and history, is another utopian scheme. Even a moderate journalist like Davis was mistaken when criticizing Americans for their attempt to redefine and redraw the map of the nation of Vietnam. It is not the Americans as Davis maintained. The true authors of such a redrawn map were the French. Therefore, we have to resolve the highlands problem without any obsessive bias connected with the past. Everything has to be studied afresh. In view of this, I wonder why we don't adopt some form of federation, a federation that includes both the *Dega* and Vietnamese nations. You know that, as an American, I can't publicly express such opinions for fear of being misunderstood by both sides."

CHAPTER TWELVE

I returned to Saigon and discovered that, after all, my last journey in the highlands was to be of no real value. The editor told me that my investigative work had to be immediately terminated. The newspaper had encountered much difficulty, difficulty coming not only from the Information Bureau, but also from the National Security Office. A summons from the latter had to be taken as a serious warning—in this case, a warning against jeopardizing the spirit of the American-Vietnamese alliance and thereby intentionally causing trouble for the government. The accusation was truly ill founded and the punishment unpredictable. Given the delicate position of the newspaper, it was clear that we were walking a very tight rope, full of danger. Many times I told myself that I could not remain silent any longer, but then what kind of noise could we effectively make by voicing our critical comments on social facts? The survival of the newspaper and the practical means of livelihood for many people depended on what I chose to do under the circumstance. But it was clear that under all circumstances, we first had to survive. It followed that the new series of articles I was working on, which had only just begun to be published, had to be canceled. It occurred to me that without the right atmosphere, it would be a long time before I resumed writing. Given the present situation I found myself in, it was doubtful that I would survive long in journalism. My mind went blank. There were no thoughts, no ideas.

I vaguely heard the sound of a door being opened. A moment later, the secretary appeared and told me that a professor had earlier in the afternoon come looking for me, just after I had taken leave of the office. He had left a business card and a note. I was surprised to see the name of Professor Hoang Thai Trung.

"So, you also know Professor Trung?" the secretary asked. On her happy face, I caught a glimpse of mischievous questioning eyes as she closed the door behind her.

Professor Trung had read my last few articles in the paper, and his attention had been very much drawn to the issues I had raised, especially the angle taken in relation to manipulation by the Americans. He expressed surprise that after only a short time engaged in journalism, I had such a firm grasp of the highlands issue and a very serious view about it. Therefore, he hoped to have a chance to meet with me again and to discuss that Promised Land within Vietnam. In his opinion, after the war ended—for which war would not eventually end—the future of Vietnam depended more on that wild territory than on the Mekong delta with its rivers and canals. I read over and over many times the lines of his note, and each time they conveyed a new thought and a new feeling. I opened my drawer and clipped the business card to the cover of the file of materials he had earlier sent, of which I had barely finished reading one third. I slipped his note into the file. In contrast to my weary thoughts only a moment before, there came again that inner urge motivat-

ing me to continue my writing before the facts became worn out
and lost their significance.

That same evening, Davis invited me to a farewell dinner for
Dr. Ross, who was returning to America. Ever since Minister
Denman had briefly mentioned Dr. Ross during my first meeting
with him, the actual role of Ross had been an intriguing question
to me. There were different, if not contradictory opinions about
the man, which rendered his background all the more fuzzy. It
would be accurate to say that under the very ordinary facade of
his day-to-day activities there lurked many formidably tricky
schemes.

Even through the well-informed Davis, I could only gather
very little information about Ross. A member of the Michigan
State University Advisory Group, Dr. Ross had been tasked to
teach political economy at the two schools of law, one at the
University of Hue and the other at Saigon University. He spoke
fluent Vietnamese, employing precise words. He entertained
friendly relations with members of the Vietnamese intelligentsia,
especially with student leaders. During the first couple of years in
Vietnam, he had been a close and reliable advisor to President
Ngo Dinh Diem. However, after disturbances caused by opposition forces, his role was questioned. This was particularly
because of his close relations with various groups, many members among which were political rivals of the Diem regime. Not
only the Central Intelligence Office—which reported directly to
the president—but also many high-ranking Vietnamese government officials sensed that underhanded incitement had been committed by the Michigan State University Advisory Group, most
notably as a result of their transparent connection to the rebellion
of a number of Thuong villages.

One after another, members of the group met with difficulties
during their stay, and were subsequently deported by the Diem
government. Dr. Ross himself had been detained by public secu-

rity people for a while, then released. He had subsequently stayed away from Vietnam and only returned after the military coup in November 1963 had toppled President Diem's regime. Presently, he appeared at many meetings of new influential groups. Well-informed people considered him a roving ambassador of Washington, wielding a lot of authority.

Dr. Ross was a close friend of General Thuyet and earned great respect from the general. For this reason, upon Ross's request, the general did not hesitate to free the students who opposed the government and who adopted an anti-American stand. He was the only American whom this group of leftist students accepted as their ally. Ross also won a lot of warm feeling from Buddhists for his support and help throughout their struggle. Davis often teasingly called Ross *Passe-Partout*—one who can pass through any door, overcome any obstacle—if only by virtue of the fact that he was simultaneously considered an ally by two opposing sides, without suffering negative consequences of this circumstance.

It being dinner time, Van Canh Restaurant was full, all tables around the dance floor occupied. Dr. Ross had telephoned to make reservations early in the afternoon; as a result, one table with five chairs was available when we arrived. Music and conversation mixed, ballooning into a big noisy clatter. We were given special service not so much because of the number of people in our group, but because Davis knew the manager well. Rumor had it that the manager's name was officially used for operation of the restaurant, while in reality this establishment was yet another financial base of one of the generals. Its clientele included all kinds of people, of different nationalities and various age groups. It was a rendezvous where political affairs were discussed and schemed, where black-market tricks were devised. Both revolution and treason could begin right here.

Dr. Ross commenced our discussion. Though he was returning to America the next day and could leave everything behind, he could not help being concerned about the student unrest originating at the medical college this morning. A kind of teach-in at the college had begun, focused upon a benign subject: It was time to restore the active role of the Vietnamese language in colleges and universities. The issue was not new, but it very much appealed to the crowd. Anger and resentment stemming from injured self-esteem found free outlet for full expression. Students sharply criticized the dependency of Vietnamese universities on a foreign language for instruction. In their view, it was high time for Vietnamese universities to belong to Vietnam, the land for which the indispensable symbol was the Vietnamese language, a mysterious invincible source of emotion that made Vietnamese strong and secure against threats of assimilation and loss of identity.

Dr. Ross addressed all of us. "What do you think of Professor Hoang Thai Trung? Myself, I think he's truly a communist. There is very clear evidence of that fact, most of all from what happened this morning."

He referred to Professor Trung's presentation during the teach-in at the medical college. The students' spontaneous demonstration immediately followed his talk, which, aside from its anti-government content, was colored with anti-American sentiment.

"Quite so," the Minister of Education agreed. "Just look at his published newspaper articles. The argument presented in them is no different from what you can read in books and newspapers from Hanoi. Many people who know him well agree with me."

"His writing itself is not worth being concerned about," Ross opined, "but its effect is palpable when thrown to the crowd directly." Ross spoke in French because Davis's Vietnamese was poor and everyone at the table spoke excellent French.

The foreign affairs minister, a rival of Professor Trung who was afraid of the professor's influence, refrained from expressing his own view. He was content with mentioning a known fact. "Professor Trung has a brother who is a high-ranking communist cadre in the north, still alive and well."

"Yes, that's true," Ross confirmed. "So I have been told by people at the University of Hue, even by General Thuyet."

The education minister chimed in: "Even if one supposes Professor Trung is a nationalist, one is surprised to see that he holds forth with only one line of argument, disparaging America and smearing our nationalism. We haven't seen him use the same sharp and sarcastic expressions to criticize the communists. Even those close to him, who want to defend him, find themselves baffled on this point."

I laughed and reminded them that Professor Trung was a Catholic. Ross, displaying his good knowledge of the issue, said that some among the Catholic circle also rejected Professor Trung, considering him as non-Christian or even as one who betrayed his religion.

"It is precisely the Christian appearance that protects him and provides him with such a safe path to tread," Ross added.

There was no close connection between Professor Trung and I. But I felt something had to be said when the accused was not present to defend himself. "The younger generations, particularly students, regard Professor Trung a progressive Catholic element," I said.

The education minister again proved himself virulently anti-communist. "There is *nothing* that can defend Professor Trung's behavior, which only benefits the communists."

The foreign affairs minister, of a sly nature, brightly smiled as he said to Ross in an ironic tone of voice, "Do you see that his ambiguous case represents a weak point in the democratic regime you Americans want to create in this country?"

Never uttering an accusation directly, always couching his thought in the language of diplomacy, the foreign affairs minister obviously was trying to knock down Professor Trung like one beats on the head of a snake.

Ross turned to me, and in a conspiratorial tone of voice whispered that this present government might not last long, and that the foreign affairs minister would then best serve as the ambassador to the United States. At the present time, when the antiwar movement led by American intellectuals was becoming intense, an eloquent diplomat like him was needed. The current ambassador was efficient, but too overenthusiastic in his defense of America—to the extent that sometimes he made people like Ross blush.

"There is one popular trick the present ambassador doesn't seem to know," Ross proclaimed. "One can go a long way with us Americans by adopting an anti-American attitude. If I very much appreciate your difficulties, I don't mind minor irritations arising from negative sentiments." In the past, Ross had apparently bluntly stated his mind on this subject to many Vietnamese.

The preordered dishes, hot from the kitchen, were brought to our table. Ross declined wine, a cocktail, or other hard liquor, preferring instead "33" beer, a little of which was enough to send a red color across his cheeks.

When he spoke again, Ross's voice was touched with humor. "The luggage I've packed for my return to America contains nothing but a few cases of this '33' beer," he said.

His big and hairy hand lifted a heavy beer mug. He gulped the amber liquid. White foam settled on one side of his moustache.

The foreign affairs minister laughed and joined in the light-hearted mood. "Everything comes down to a matter of habit. I myself cannot stand American cigarettes. Whenever I go abroad, I have to carry along a couple of packs of blue Bastos made in Vietnam."

I gathered that that was the first and only thing American to which he could not adapt himself.

The conversation during mealtime followed that line of trifling chitchat. I eventually asked the foreign affairs minister about the piece of news that General Thuyet might be replaced by someone else. He confirmed it and explained that the replacement could be the first step taken by the Saigon government in an attempt to regain centralized authority and power.

The reason Saigon had previously asked for the general's help in controlling the city of Hue was because he was originally from that area, being a member of the former royal family, and also a Buddhist—the attributes that made him an insider and might serve him well in dealing with the local population. Saigon judged that only General Thuyet had the guts to suppress the leftist student groups and the Buddhists in Hue. At the same time, Saigon's scheme was to use the struggling Buddhists as an excuse to oust him in the event he failed in his task of suppressing them, which the central authority believed would be the case. A military commander forever obsessed by the role of hero, General Thuyet had accepted the suggestion that he be transferred to I Corps. Following his transfer, the government's policy toward the highlands underwent major changes.

With regard to the students who were causing trouble in Hue, the foreign affairs minister characterized them as an unruly bunch, and believed that the only way to restore law and order in that city was to draft them all into military service.

"Well, come to think of it," he said, "there's nothing General Thuyet is afraid to do. If anyone would dare adopt such a measure, he would."

The education minister was concerned about the same issue. "This is what I think," he offered. "After the Revolution of '63, the force of the youths has been like a torrent that bursts its banks and can't be stopped. There are no constructive activities into which they can channel the energy and characteristic enthusiasm of youth. Moreover, being young and inexperienced, they are vulnerable to outside influence, and undoubtedly have been incited by the communists. In my view, all the recent agitations and troubles result from these reasons. For their participant role in the overthrow of the Diem regime, they have credited themselves with revolutionary merit making, and have become impatient and arrogant. To stabilize the political atmosphere, we must find some way to keep them busy. You may have noticed that they hold demonstrations and teach-ins with zealousness only at the beginning of an academic year. At the end of the year, too busy preparing for final exams, they abandon all such activities. The responsibility of the government right now is to make them preoccupied with the social life within their schools and colleges. But the main obstacle to this is the lack of an adequate budget."

Dr. Ross nodded knowingly and said with enthusiasm, "The students themselves are advocating a movement to commit themselves to the service of the rural areas. We can make use of their own noble motivations."

The education minister was not finished with his laments. "Look," he said, "with allocations for education being only 4 percent of the national budget, I can't do anything better than I already am."

"Don't worry," Dr. Ross assured him, "AID funds can compensate for the shortfall. The main requirement is that innovations must originate from the government of Vietnam itself."

The foreign affairs minister quickly offered his advice. "Hold on," he said. "Whatever bears the trademark of the government can easily arouse biased suspicion. Youth activities will best take shape within their own circle. At least it should appear that way on the surface."

Dr. Ross was in full support of the minister's view. "You are right, Minister," he agreed. "The psychological issue is a big obstacle. As regards the budgetary matter, I can find ways to send funds to them in the guise of aid from private American citizens. What the students are concerned about are ulterior political motives."

The foreign affairs minister had a more optimistic assessment. "You people loudly revile corruption in the government. But hand out millions of piastres to those student leaders and see what happens. Sooner or later they will all burn themselves out, long since having forgotten political agendas."

That comment made Dr. Ross more enthusiastic.

"Education Minister, have you an idea to start with?" Ross asked. "I know a number of student leaders in Saigon, Dalat, and Hue. I can ask them to help you."

"Thank you. There are many details that need to be discussed and tackled. I am sure I will have to meet with you many more times."

"I am going back to America for three months to enjoy my summer vacation. But I can be back here at any time, if necessary. When you need something, please just let me know. I will do my best to assist you."

In spite of Ross's assurance, the education minister was still full of doubt. "It's possible to do what you suggest in Saigon. But so far as other areas are concerned, my authority is limited because of the regional generals."

"It can be done; don't you worry," Ross confirmed. "I am very close to many generals. I know you are concerned about the Hue area. But I think the real difficulty lies in Saigon. I guarantee your success up in Hue."

The increasing volume of noise from conversation and laughter at the surrounding tables made it impossible for us to continue the discussion. Soon, the evening's entertainment began. The lights went out amidst rounds of excited applause. Into a spotlight lithely walked a young woman wrapped in a gown of intense red. Very slowly, naturally, elegantly, each part of her body was freed of its covering, revealing in her pose an image suggestive of a lotus bud. The perfect beauty of a statue drew frenzied, hot, desirous stares from the men. The blossom unfolded in the pool of red about its stem. Her skillful style in executing each gesture strongly aroused the audience. Loud rock music in the background gave rhythm to the movement of a naked provocative body, teasingly whirling around, now flailing the loose red gown as if burning flame leaping from a fire. The scene was accentuated by noisy foot stamping and banging of hands on tables by a number of soldiers. Perhaps these men had just returned from some battlefield, feeling alive once more after moments facing death. Only woman and sexual desire could pull them back into life.

CHAPTER THIRTEEN

Saigon's atmosphere was riddled with electricity, seemingly poised for a coup d'état. In anticipation of trouble, the government decided to do away with all celebration ceremonies on National Day. The ruling power also strictly banned troop movements from one area to another, and ordered all commanders to stay put wherever they were stationed. These adjustments suggested that the focus was on General Thuyet in the Danang-Hue area, a man who had a number of combat units—airborne divisions, marines—ready to follow his bidding. As for General Tri in II Corps, the official orders robbed him of an opportunity to lead a parade along Saigon streets, with himself riding an elephant followed by Thuong soldiers wielding machetes and colorfully dressed in their traditional outfits. In the midst of such tense and heated atmospherics, the controversial tragedy of Dakto, with almost six hundred innocent people killed, lost its significance, except for those directly connected with it, among whom was General Thuyet.

In fact, the writer-advisor to the general looked me up when he came to Saigon. He told me the general was very concerned about recent developments in the Central Highlands, that he was indignant and angry with regard to secret manipulations behind the scenes. The general still saw himself responsible for the Thuong peoples, peoples who had pledged loyalty to him, and although he was posted away from them, he wanted to continue attending to their welfare.

"The general likes your writing very much," said the writer. "If only you could move to Hue, start a paper there, and bring together some other brother journalists."

I was reminded of Professor Trung's suggestion that I go to Hue and revive a certain newspaper, the ultimate purpose of this paper being far different from what the general had in mind. If Như Nguyện and I decided to move to Hue, it would certainly not be because of my promise to revive or create either paper. Rather, the move would signal my final departure from journalism in hopes of resuming my painting.

"Excuse me," the writer said, abruptly changing the subject, "have you seen superior monk Pháp Viên again recently? If possible, would you arrange for the two of us to meet with him? It would be more convenient if you were present. I am sure you know I came to Saigon this time as the general's envoy."

He informed me that even though the Buddhist resistance movement had been suppressed, its spirit still smoldered in the Buddhist population. It was as if General Thuyet were sitting on a basin of burning charcoal, deceptively covered with layers of ash. The general could not once and for all settle the trouble without the collaborating support of the superior monk. It was obvious, then, that the writer's mission was none other than to secure the spiritual support required by the general.

"But what will the general say to explain his harsh treatment of the master's disciples?" I asked.

After a moment of reflection, the writer gave his reply slowly, carefully, and in sufficient detail as to be sure there could be no misunderstanding. "We must admit that this time the Buddhists went too far. The general was in an awkward position, as he could not go against policies established in Saigon. When you think about it, it must be clear that without the general's concessions, the struggle could not have remained active for so long as it has. Moreover, the master must have realized that the counteraction schemes did not come from the general or those under the general's authority. These schemes were the work of the colonel commanding the Military Security Service, the counterintelligence arm of the ARVN that reports directly to the Office of the Presidency. In fact, the major component of the counteraction forces was the Police Field Force unit, which is directly under the command of the National Police Directorate."

It was my understanding that a person of many principles like monk Pháp Viên was hardly inclined to accept a compromise, even one proposed by General Thuyet. The only hope remaining to the general was that when the struggle failed, the monk would again become flexible enough to adapt to the new situation. During the last few days of his hunger strike, when he grew very weak, the monk seemed to have seen things more clearly and became quite aware of the exhaustion felt by the Buddhist public. They still revered him, but at the same time were too tired to continue with the struggle wholeheartedly. They could only muster enough energy to come and prostrate to him as to a living Buddha, praying that he would live and hence would not abandon them. The situation was so hopeless that a few people even considered monk Pháp Viên cruel, in that he could abandon Buddhist followers but would never give up the aim of the Buddhist struggle.

I was brought back from my pondering to the present by a sudden question from the writer. "Excuse me," he said, "what do you have in mind by considering work in Hue with Mr. Trung?

There is plenty of evidence showing that he has communication
with the communists. The general has the evidence in hand."

He did not tell me anything sensational, like a new discovery.
I had heard the same thing from the foreign affairs minister and
also from Dr. Ross. I still had faith in my relations with Mr.
Trung, and did not think there was anything to reconsider with
regard to this matter. Anyway, my planned move to Hue was for
quite a different purpose.

I explained this to the writer. "If I wanted to continue my job
as a journalist, I would not have to take the effort to go all the way
up to Hue; I can do it well enough right here. My girl friend praises Hue without reservation, and I myself also want to live there.
To me, quietude is a necessary ingredient for a proper atmosphere
in which to return to painting."

The writer gave me a strange look. His voice humorous, he
said. "A quiet Vĩ Dạ village is there, to be sure, but it's not certain you can be at peace living and painting beside such a well-
known person as her."

Though Như Nguyện spent little time in Hue, it was exactly
as the writer said: the whole city was aware of her notoriety. As
always, I felt uncomfortable when someone mentioned her, and
thought that the harsh public opinion in a way had drawn me
closer to her. As though sensing my discomfiture, the writer
turned to another subject. He related to me events associated with
the recent awarding of literary prizes performed in Hue.

"The good will of the government was there, to be sure," he
said, "but care should be taken to consider the real talent of writers. A million piastres' worth of prizes should not have been
given to the authors of a bunch of anti-communist propaganda
writings of no literary value. In my opinion, before we talk about
the content and purpose of a piece of writing, we should be mind-
ful that the vehicle which carries it must be worthy of attention. I
am talking about the art of creating literature."

"As it appears now, to satisfy both requirements at the same time is beyond the capability of an artist."

Apparently not sensing the sarcasm in my statement, the writer continued in his serious tone of voice. "You know, there are numerous materials out there ready for use in the creation of great works of literature. They are not exclusively related to the situation in Vietnam; rather, they encompass the future tragedy of humankind. Many times I have asked myself whether Vietnamese creative powers, corresponding to our short stature and small bones, are inadequate for the production of great works."

"The tragedy of Europe," I suggested, "brought humankind great works of literature only after several years had elapsed following the Second World War."

As though he had just been shown a way out, the writer seized the moment to elaborate on his belief. "I hope this is so here, too," he concurred. "We need time for things to settle down. A writer cannot create when he's caught up in social upheavals like those at present."

Conversations with the writer never failed to open up distant and immense horizons. One had to admit that at his age, his voice still retained much power of attraction, even to the younger generation. He next invited me to partake of a meal with himself and another close advisor to General Thuyet, the law professor who was a member of the Committee for Postwar Economic Development, a U.S.-sponsored agency. I had to decline the invitation, as I already had previous arrangements with Như Nguyện. I promised him, as requested, that, if the government allows me access to Master Pháp Viên, I would try my best to arrange for a meeting with the monk.

In no time at all after this conversation with the writer-advisor, there came news from the city of Hue that General Thuyet had heavy-handedly dealt with protesting students and Buddhists, while in Saigon monk Pháp Viên had had to submit himself to government protection, a euphemism for house arrest. By myself, I visited the master in his prevailing circumstances, and succeeded in writing up a five-thousand-word interview with him, which the editor-in-chief considered an extraordinary feat for a nonprofessional journalist like myself. Unlike what he had conveyed to the foreign press, this was the first time the reserved monk agreed to openly express his attitude toward communism. He showed himself a revolutionary fighter having strong reasons to believe in inevitable victory for his Buddhist struggle. Nonetheless, he thought the struggle would go on for a long time because, up in Hue, it was not supported by any military forces that could stage a coup to change the situation, as might be the case in Saigon.

Indeed, what the Buddhist movement hoped for had not materialized, and excessiveness in the struggle had led to, so to speak, a confused front and an exhausted rear. Saigon was still calm except for scattered demonstrations by women and children, one leading to the next, which were experienced by them as little more than big games. In addition, there were signs of internal division within the Buddhist organization.

I agreed to give Davis priority in utilization of the interview report. It was the only way I could be sure that the written words would remain intact, for, with Davis, there would be no necessity of going through censorship by the Vietnamese Information Bureau, which would surely cut and delete the text beyond recognition. Davis asked me to check the translated version before he sent it directly to the United States through the teletype machine.

It was a Friday afternoon in Saigon, or morning in Washington, D.C., where it was too early for anyone—except perhaps those who chose journalism as their career—to get up and begin any serious work. We sat and smoked in Davis's office, inattentively gazing at paintings on the wall and waiting for the machine to swallow up the rest of the tape containing news items that had to be dispatched. The black teletype machine, with a dimly lit dot of light, lay quietly at work, its sound reverberating like waves splashing against a windless shore. Near a window, by the warm intrusion of light, the teletypist punched out the last lines of the interview on a roll of paper spilling down onto the floor. Looking through a glass door and over the terrace beyond, I noted on the other side of the street that the Caravelle Hotel was brightly lit, even though Tu Do Street was emptied of foreign visitors, most probably because of the present insecure condition of Saigon.

The phone rang. Information came in about the progress of an ongoing Buddhist demonstration. I took leave of Davis and hurriedly rushed to the streets below, finding myself among confused traffic that ran helter-skelter. Restaurants were closed. Pedestrians were in a panic. From one end of Le Loi Street, beginning at Fountain Circle in front of City Hall, all the way down to Quach Thi Trang Square in front of the central Bến Thành Market were seen dozens of big trucks and armored personnel carriers filled with troops fully equipped with weapons and wearing metal helmets. Alongside them were fire engines equipped with water cannon, police jeeps, and also jeeps marked with painted white stars belonging to the American military police. The atmosphere was stifling, filled with the threat of suppressive engagement, recalling the heated environment surrounding the student demonstrations against the dictatorial Diem regime in August of '63.

The demonstrating group consisted of no more than a hundred women and children, barefooted, their clothes soaking wet, holding bricks and stones and sticks. Some among them were in possession of nylon bags to protect themselves against tear gas. Seemingly fearless, together they marched. Their shouts echoed through the streets. Bulky banners displayed complaints and demands. Pulsated with echoing shouts and cheers, a whole section of the city turned into an arena where every impulse was given free rein. A great number of press correspondents, as well as curious people, formed a tight human belt around the demonstrators. This wave of humanity was stopped at an intersection, at which point there began a rain of bricks and stones hurling at the police, all of whom ran away without responding in kind.

The growing crowd again moved forward, triumphant, feeling fermented in confrontation. The wind stretched the banners and whipped them every which way, making the slim bodies holding them slightly swayed, staggered. There suddenly appeared before the surging body a target in the form of an unattended jeep painted with white stars. A group of children demonstrators rushed for it. So many weak arms together were powerful enough to eventually turn the vehicle on its side, its gas tank bursting into flames. The hot flames shot up in the midst of reddened eyes and shouts and screams.

From afar, the urgent warning sound of a siren came closer, bringing up behind it truckloads of soldiers equipped with shields, tear gas canisters, and bulky gas masks. Tear gas canisters were thrown into the crowd, creating empty spots among the aggregation. Several American correspondents, hanging on to their cameras, staggered as if drunk. A child, sneaking through a gap between the soldier's legs, got hold of a tear gas canister and was about to hurl it toward a fire engine, but made a misstep and fell down. The crowd was pushed by police into adjacent alleys. Fire hoses splashed water onto the burning jeep.

Across the large breadth of street there remained only the soldiers, a few news correspondents with swollen red eyes, and a confusion of trash, bricks, and stones. But again there echoed in the distance the sound of a siren; the demonstrators seemed to have regathered in another section of the city. A hundred children fighters were strong enough to create disorder all over the city. This was another new face of the war, one that might be too new for Davis's comprehension. In all the streets the demonstration had passed through, big garbage piles burned high, while up above reverberated the deafening noise of jet aircraft flying low.

I stopped by the general hospital for some first aid to my teary and sore eyes, and there ran into Davis. He had also witnessed the demonstration and in the melee got his forehead nicked by a stone. His eyes were swollen and red. Davis asked me to help him get access to a telephone so he could call his paper's office. When leaving the telephone room, he appeared really tired. I suddenly realized clearly that Davis was not in the same league with other foreign journalists. They were a rather large group, most of whom were young, impatient, and disposed to action, who lived rich comfortable lives in a Saigon that bore few concrete signs of the war. Their particular zeal was absent in Davis, who lived privately and quietly. His American friends and acquaintances compared him to a bamboo stalk standing alone, away from the clump. Two flights of steps led us to a nice room. Davis dropped his whole weight on the couch, turned and talked to me in a sad voice.

"What more do you think the Americans must do here?" he asked.

Not waiting for my reply, he continued, his voice weary. "The Americans may shed their blood in the highlands and in muddy rice fields to defeat the communists and achieve great victories. But they have their hands tied experiencing one defeat after another in the cities. It would seem that it takes only a small number of women and a group of unarmed teenagers to numb all firepower, topple a government, and cause trouble even for the U.S."

"It seems your sole concern is about the Americans' victory or defeat," I observed. "Obviously, to the Vietnamese people, that's not the issue. They don't want to see Vietnam a battlefield, and at this point they agonize over the question of what they must do to ensure the survival and future of their country."

Still in the same bitter tone of voice, Davis continued voicing his thought. "I am thinking of those American soldiers who must remain in the jungle, participate in battles where they must kill or be killed, of those who have been injured, of those who have witnessed the fall of their comrades. What would they think and feel were they to set foot in the city only to be stoned, to see with their own eyes slogans and banners asking them to return to their own country?"

I could not help but smile at his words. I wanted to tell him that though he had lived here for a decade, he still did not understand the Vietnamese any better than when he had arrived.

"I have heard a few Americans angrily say that we Vietnamese are ungrateful," I replied. "You Americans cannot see anything beyond equating the anti-American sentiments generated by the impact of your Army upon Vietnam with opposition to America itself, its larger agenda—but that is not the real issue. To an intellectual Vietnamese like myself, this war, in and of itself, carries the whole weight of being an international problem, an adventurous experiment full of danger, for which the solution cannot depend purely on firepower. The major impasse lies in the ideological dogmatism long ago developed by both sides. It's time both become conscious of the fact that war destroys everything, including the dreams of a people, their future. So, both sides must try to wake up and find a way out of the deadlock.

"As for that group of women and children, they represent our desperation, our exhaustion after twenty years of conflict. They will keep on demanding one thing and another, demanding anything but the devastation of war and the finality of death. They urge one another to get into the streets, to shout and to fight, to struggle with all their desperate energy. You must understand what that force indicates. There is a great Vietnamese writer who calls these women and children fragments of bombs, shell casings, shards scattered upon battlefields, spent, forgotten, inanimate. Given this state of being, the question of gratitude or ingratitude is irrelevant, don't you think?"

Davis was silent with his thoughts. He seemed genuinely concerned with the complexity of the issue.

"It's not true that all Vietnamese condemn or denounce America," I continued. "But the imprint of foreigners on their homeland, growing more and more pronounced as the days go by, gives them pain in their hearts. To them, each Viet Cong being killed means the death of another Vietnamese. Some people insist that this is an invasion by the North, but essentially it is a civil war, an internecine war. For enlightened Vietnamese, it's not a matter of choice between the two sides, but a matter of finding an acceptable solution."

Confounded by the perplexity of the problem, Davis shrugged his shoulders. He walked toward the window. "I have been considered an expert on Vietnam, but really, at this point, I don't seem to understand anything."

We both felt weary. Whatever subject we broached seemed to promise no positive future. As he turned to the desk by the window, Davis called out to me, his voice pleasantly surprised.

"Lo! You still keep this photo?" he exclaimed. "It's one I took three years ago."

I shook my head and reminded him that we were in the office of a friend of mine who worked in the hospital. This friend had been a faithful Buddhist, a person zealously participating in the Buddhist struggle in 1963. But after that, he returned to the life of a genuine student, and did not have much regard for monks of the present day.

Gazing at the photo, Davis declared that it had been the first and only time he had agreed to witness a prearranged suicide. I promptly observed that there seemed to be some misconception on the part of Western journalists when they called self-immolation suicide, which was not at all what it meant in Buddhist philosophy.

Davis conceded this. "I have been told that much—early this year after my recent book was published in America. I received a letter from Giác Nghiệp, a young Vietnamese Buddhist monk and an excellent disciple of Master Pháp Viên, who had studied at Yale University. He objected to the term "suicide" used in my description of a monk's self-immolation. According to monk Giác Nghiệp, self-immolation is not the same as suicide, much less an expression of an attitude of denouncement and opposition. Suicide is the cowardly act of running away from a dilemma whereas self-immolation requires a conscious decision to confront it with courage. Moreover, from the Buddhist point of view, life is not confined to the existence of the physical body. To tell the truth, I can't in any way understand and accept these kinds of arguments, which are both new and alien to me. I am a Christian. Though I don't go to church often, I have a deep faith in the religion. To me, faith is your pure beliefs; there can be no room in it for human attempts to explain the will of God."

Throughout his many years of living in Vietnam, Davis was highly credited for his knowledge of Asian affairs, but he achieved fame during the Buddhist struggle under the Diem regime. It was also during that time that he earned a Pulitzer Prize for journalism.

His eyes distant in recollection, Davis confided in me. "You know, a month before the actual event, I had heard rumors about a plan for self-immolation of two monks who fought for five Buddhist aspirations; but then it slipped my mind. Suddenly, one morning, I received a special phone call from the young monk Giác Nghiệp telling me what was about to happen. This privileged information was such a great honor for a journalist, and naturally I became well known as a result of that. The photos I took of the event appeared in newspapers all over the world and evoked a tremendous emotional response. It was also because of those photos that the American press collectively criticized the anti-

Buddhist policies of President Diem, while Buddhist nations in anger protested against the U.S. China distributed all over Asia, Africa, and Latin America millions of copies of the photos to propagandize what the Chinese dubbed a self-immolation act to oppose American imperialism. As for me, to tell you the truth, after that instance of glory, my conscience became haunted with remorse. Subsequently, I was again informed beforehand of other self-immolation events, but I chose to absent myself. That surprised many people, especially my colleagues, but in this situation I had no choice."

Greenish-brown eyes focused deep in memory, the voice of Davis alone touched the quiet night. "I have not forgotten the image that moved me to tears: that of a monk with a facial expression of gentle loving-kindness, a monk who looked like a living Buddha, sitting not on a Buddha's dais, but in the lap of a fierce red flame that enveloped his entire body. His face contracted because of the intense heat, but it was a marvel that he sat calmly, motionless in the glowing flame, while around him people wept uncontrollably and screamed hysterically."

It was past midnight. The silence around us was unusual, eerie—a paucity of traffic noise, absence of the sound of artillery, no thunder of a distant air strike. The office phone rang loudly, startling us. On the other end of the line, a police doctor said that a group of demonstrators, in defiance of the curfew, was marching toward the national radio station, and that the army had been given orders to disperse them. We could not tell from this what would transpire, but we thought we ought to be there nonetheless. This would be another sleepless night for us both, which marked the beginning of another week sure to be filled with bricks and stones, tear gas canisters, a multitude of tears.

CHAPTER FOURTEEN

BBC broadcast the news that a quiet, bloodless, military overhaul, approaching a purge, had occurred in Saigon, led by General Thuyet, who had come down from I Corps for that purpose. Immediately after the conclusion of the act, the purpose of which was to remove some old generals, General Thuyet, accompanied by several Young Turks, paid a visit to the American Embassy to explain the reasons for the event, reasons he referred to as internal corrections aimed at restoring strength and power to the army. In truth, the generals involved in this internal correction affair, after their united efforts to suppress the resistance activities of the Buddhists, had shown signs of incipient rivalry and potential fractionation. Saigon displayed its ordinary appearance, this time without pocket demonstrations staged by women and children. During the evening of the same day, General Thuyet gave an excellent speech on national radio, addressing his hope that the dawn of a Nasser-type social revolution had shown its face.

Following in the general's wake, the writer-advisor hurriedly came to Saigon. Upon meeting with me again, he attempted to explain the dilemma faced by the general, which had forced him to use drastic measures against the student and Buddhist resistance in Hue.

As regards the superior monk Pháp Viên, perhaps having realized that the struggle could not continue after his death, he terminated his hopeless hunger strike that had been prolonged for many days. Upon return to his pagoda, he was no more than a skeleton, his heart heavy with bitter experience from a period of intense struggle. This was the first time since the so-called "'63 Revolution" that a prevailing government had succeeded in overpowering the Buddhists. Another occurrence that the master had not expected was the formation of a clear division among his followers in the final stage of the resistance.

And then there was the lack of impartiality—or, rather, too much pragmatism—on the part of the American Embassy. With regard to the reality of this issue, the American Embassy was keenly aware that the Buddhist resistance was a determining factor in the success of the '63 Revolution that toppled President Diem. Its leader, monk Pháp Viên, had been hailed by the American press as a person who touched the American heart, but after that successful coup d'état, realizing that the Buddhist movement was excessive and hence an unsuitable vehicle for American policy in Vietnam, the American Embassy did not extend any support, while the Buddhists had been led to believe it would provide assistance. Naturally, monk Pháp Viên became very disappointed with the Americans. Since his return to the pagoda, he had withdrawn from the limelight and refused all contact with the outside, especially with the press.

The morning after the military overhaul, a press conference, chaired by General Thuyet, was held by the Council of Generals drawn from the Joint General Staff, the supreme command of the South Vietnamese Army, Marines, Air Force, and Navy. Nothing new was added that had not been said in the general's speech on the radio the night before. At the end of this official public appearance of the generals, I chanced to meet General Tri again. Courteously, I congratulated him on his promotion. The general smiled halfheartedly and displayed no trace of joy. Maybe he understood that gaining another star was also a sign of old age, which signaled to younger generals that they could retire him. He no longer wore the imperious arrogant air he had displayed in the highlands, but instead seemed inclined to court the press. General Tri mentioned my series of investigative articles on Dakto printed in the paper, some of which he had read in full.

"I followed that series," he said. "The first impression I have is that you want to place the whole burden of responsibility for the tragedy on our side. As a military man of honor, I never deny due responsibility. But, truly, in this case, we did our best to help them relocate, and as to what happened afterwards, we had no control over it."

I explained to the general that the series of articles actually had not been completely written, that my only desire was to simply expose facts, and that it would require a book to cover interpretation and critical analysis of those facts. I was still hoping to write such a book.

"We can only understand the tragedy in the larger context of the future of the Central Highlands," I added.

He did not seem to catch on to what I had said, so I did not go further into it. From the professional habit of not letting go of opportunities for information gathering, I asked the general about the story of the Green Belt, the strategic defensive belt of SFOBs created by American Special Forces and strung across South Vietnam, Laos, northern Thailand, and into northern Burma.

"I've heard about that secondhand," he replied. "Personally, I don't know how true the thesis is. Politics, by nature, is dubious, and often goes beyond observable facts. In my opinion, leadership in the Central Highlands should now be a political role, not a military one, but I myself am a purely military person, so I cannot fulfill this new role. For that reason, I have already sent the central government a petition explaining my concern."

I asked General Tri what he thought about the possibility of General Thuyet returning to the highlands and of his new influence in the central government.

"I have also thought about such a possibility," answered General Tri. "However, I've heard many voices of protest against it, including that of the Americans. This is for your ears only: the central government does not much cherish his obstinacy. But there is one thing about him all must recognize and respect, and that is he is very firm and upright. I personally will always prefer a comrade-in-arms like General Thuyet."

I repeated to General Tri the observation made by the minister Denman that the American military circle, and even the American Embassy, quite agreed with the appointment of General Tri to replace General Thuyet, and that as a result, the American press subsequently seemed less inclined to criticize the Vietnamese government.

"But it is precisely because of this replacement," the general said wearily, "that I am caught in the middle between many opposing sides. The highlands problem is still there. How can we tell for how long the area can be pacified and when the latent explosives lying about will erupt? Because of many conflicting interests, until now, there have not appeared satisfactory solutions to the problems endemic to the Central Highlands."

Not wanting to specifically mention the captain from Bui Chu who had guided me to the scene of the massacre, I attributed to public opinion the captain's argument that the Vietnamese government had made a mistake in entrusting to the Americans full authority to distribute aid to the Thuong refugees. General Tri did not respond heatedly, as might have been expected. He gently justified his position.

"I am well aware of the controversy," he began, "and I am not blind to the one truth about the Thuong people: they obey and feel grateful only to those who put food into their mouths. The Americans know this as well, and they utilize the circumstance when they attempt to monopolize the effort to win the hearts and minds of the Thuong. General Thuyet was not successful with the policy of having aid handled by the Vietnamese authorities; it clearly did not work well, and the problem of aid distribution became more and more difficult. As of now, the compromise is to entrust the relief operation to Minister Denman—and his wife, of course. As an almost Vietnamized American, the minister has won goodwill and respect from a majority of the Thuong population, and as a result it can be seen that everything is proceeding with care and quite satisfactorily."

I smiled at the idea of Vietnamization being applied to the minister. Aside from changes that could be observed on the outside, his pragmatic way of thinking still bore the essential mark of an American personality. The image of a blue-eyed and red-bearded clergyman energetically preaching about existence of God and about hopes for happiness in an afterlife in front of a large flock of believers, humble and poverty-stricken, transported me back through the last few centuries of human civilization. The events of those times revealed a ruthlessness unpleasant to think about, but one had to admit that the milieu was full of seduction and excitement for adventurous souls like Tacelosky and the American Special Forces soldiers.

General Tri inquired about the journalist Davis. "I was surprised to meet such a polite and modest American journalist like him," he commented. "The Dakto massacre must have made him very sad."

"Davis cried upon hearing the terrible news . . . Incidentally, I wonder what General Casey, who replaces General Hunting at An Khe, thinks about the highlands' situation."

"General Casey has suggested a joint investigation of overall security conditions, but I don't think this will go anywhere, because, aside from commanding the First Air Cavalry Division, this general has no authority whatsoever over American Special Forces camps. The irony is that the acting American 'Consul to the Highlands' is not General Casey, but Tacelosky, who is a perverse colonialist. It is this same Tacelosky who has corrupted many good American friends upon their arrival in the Central Highlands. In truth, he is afraid only of General Thuyet."

It would seem that the necessity of having a hero for the highlands was imperative. However, if, as General Tri said, the general controlling the highlands had to assume a political role, there was no certainty this would suit General Thuyet's capabilities, unless he received constant advice from his writer-advisor, and the law professor he was close to who was involved with the Committee for Postwar Economic Development.

A bell rang for a meeting of some sort. I left General Tri with his insistent and awkward preoccupation. Exiting the Joint General Staff compound, I noticed on the flagpole in the parade grounds the fluttering standard of General Thuyet, who would soon return to I Corps after having accomplished his special mission in Saigon. A sulfur light beat through dark clouds patchworked across an oppressive sky, a light that caused a headache in all those, like myself, without protection of a hat.

Back at my paper's office, I was told that Kux, a German professor from Berlin University, had just returned from Hue and wanted to see me. Kux had been stuck up there for many days because of the uninterrupted Buddhist struggle. He appeared clearly tired as a result of the rigors of this trip. Kux was a very close friend of Davis. He was writing a book entitled *The Road to Asia*, which was a research work on Buddhism and communism in Asia. His trip to Vietnam was for the purpose of this research. Introduced by Davis, who was off in Thailand,

Kux had looked me up at my paper's offices and asked for my guidance. I had spent a busy week taking him around to visit various places and the leaders of major religious bodies. I was too preoccupied with work in my office to leave Saigon, so Kux had had to organize his subsequent solo trips on his own, among them the one to Hue.

Toward midnight tonight, Kux was to leave for Tokyo.

In the afternoon, I took him to the outskirts of Saigon, where I expressed regrets that he had not been able spend a period in the countryside, as, in truth, the war inflicted significant damage only there.

"Collateral damage is inherent to every war. I had such experience in Germany," Kux said.

I asked Kux what he thought of Buddhism in Vietnam, especially after his visit to Hue.

"I feel that a number of Buddhist leaders were mistaken when they conceived their power base in the image of a brigade of holy war fighters," he reflected. "To me, Asians are by nature moderate and tolerant, more or less influenced by Taoism. In consequence, they cannot become extremists like believers of Islam or of some other religions—which is a fact that has been proven by history. Just as many people thought, the forces opposing communism do not lie only in the Christianity that came from the Western world. I am thinking about a kind of spirituality that is deep-rooted in the social life of the multitude, which has a determinative influence on future conditions in Asia. South Vietnam, at present, is not simply a test battlefield where nationalism and communism clash. It is also a challenging experimental ground for the Buddhists to reckon their real strength: I am talking about engaged Buddhism."

On our way to the outskirts of Saigon, we found a greater presence of the police and the army in the streets, and at several public offices. This was no doubt in the aftermath of the workshop and subsequent riotous demonstration targeting the national radio station, which had occurred this morning—both initiated by the General Association of Students. Leaving the city behind, our car ran very smoothly along the highway. Kux asked about the construction projects we passed by.

"They are the recent implementation of projects drafted in President Diem's time," I answered. "Not to mention the mistakes committed by his regime, we have to admit that President Diem was a very far-sighted person. That's something we cannot say of the present leadership."

Kux expressed surprise. "You are the first person I have met here who mentions President Diem in a tone of respect."

"No, that's not quite correct. In the last years of his presidency, I took a stand against him. However, as friends or foes who loved or hated him, everyone, including the Americans, have to bow in reverence for a few of his personal human qualities. Those supporting the '63 Revolution deny everything good about President Diem, but I believe that history will judge him more fairly than it has during the first few years after his fall."

Kux laughed and asked if I was not afraid of being labeled as antirevolutionary.

I remained calm. "Everyone realizes that the collapse of his regime was inevitable, and I myself think his death was necessary to avoid a chain of disturbing events. But it's still too early now to accuse or defend whatever has only recently happened."

On our way back, Kux invited me to join him for dinner at the Caravelle Hotel where he stayed. We both did not have the time to go elsewhere to a Vietnamese restaurant. The Caravelle was an ultramodern hotel serving as the headquarters for the crowd of international press correspondents. There could be no more extreme elegance than that of its lobby, a world of ostentation and diaphanousness. From the high-up clusters of delicate yellow lights gently spread the lumen of luxury, down over marble slabs to the carpets tread upon below. A space of cold contradictions.

"When I first arrived in Saigon," Kux said, "I was over-whelmed with many impressions. For one, Saigon suggests the image of a Russian princess after the proletarian revolution, who had to wander all the way to Paris where she attempted to live in a haughty noble fashion to mask her reduced circumstances. I am sure the American dollar enlarged and improved the whole city in a flash. But all the new features are still fresh, having yet not a personality."

From the tenth floor of the hotel, Saigon appeared fragment-ed, a matrix of slots dotted with light. Silhouettes of ships were seen lying tired, puffing up smoke, waiting for the next deposit of cargo before leaving port. The evening sky was heavy with dark shadow movements. In the direction of Tan Son Nhat Airport, once in awhile, flares were shot into the air, shining on columns of white smoke. From here, only that much of the war could be seen.

Kux wondered about my appearing to be deep in thought. My feelings at this moment were really confused, and I told him so.

"Let me see how I can explain this to you," I said. "Perhaps I want to tell you that when you extend your vision beyond and away from these high-rise buildings around you, you see down below nothing but the poverty and cramped living conditions of the common people. All four thousand Vietnamese villages are like that. The effects of the American dollar do not reach far."

Kux smiled a knowing half-smile. "Isn't that the way American aid always goes? It never reaches far."

Through tinted glass panes, the electric lights turned the leaves of the trees along the boulevards a reddish color. I imag-ined that at this time of night streetwalkers were waiting under the trees to solicit clients. From the airport, Phantom jets took off, throwing behind them sparks of fire and thundering sound. Their echo rattled the glass windows. Then silence reigned, only to be broken by Kux.

"Triet," he called my attention, "at noon today, on my way in from the airport, I stopped by a steam bath, its name being something like Bao An. The establishment is elegant, and best of all, it's not a brothel in disguise. I stepped into a room that was so hot and steamy that everything was blurred. Listening to voices, I knew only men were present, most of them Americans. All of us were naked, but the steam was so thick I could not see anything further than half a meter from me. Suddenly the big form of an American loomed before me. 'How long have you been here? From what state?' he asked. I told him I am not American, but a German journalist. 'Then you must really be a happy person, as you have no obligations here,' he observed. Surprised, I asked him what he meant. As he rubbed a towel against his body, the man answered vaguely: 'Because I am a pilot—day in, day out carrying bombs to drop everywhere and anywhere, including north of the demilitarized zone.' His voice was truly weary and insensate. After those few words, he turned around and soon merged into a cluster of other Americans."

It was a bare story, with feelings sunk below the surface.

In the same dry tone, Kux continued. "He and I did not see each other's face clearly. We won't recognize each other if we meet again on the street. The encounter was rather curious, and it makes me think. I wonder about American pilots like him who drop bombs every day, fighting with no apparent conviction like that. What will they think when they have to fly and drop bombs over North Vietnam, or when they are shot down? When that happens, does President Johnson or does Christ take responsibility for their deaths?"

If only Kux had encountered American Special Forces soldiers, I thought. In his eyes, American soldiers were all sadly engaged in the Vietnam War, with bewildered and lost feelings.

Như Nguyện traced me by telephone and said that she and two friends were waiting for me at my newspaper's offices. Kux and I took an elevator down to his room on the fifth floor where I bid good-bye and stated my regret that I could not see him off as promised, even though his departure point, the Pan Am office and airport limousine service, was near the hotel.

CHAPTER FIFTEEN

It was a day of calamity and grief for the American Special Forces in Asia. During the same day, two Air America planes were downed: one in the northeast of Laos on the Plain of Jars in Xieng Khouang, with a group of fourteen Special Forces soldiers onboard, all considered missing in action; the other, a STOL, a Short Take Off and Landing plane, was shot down in northern Burma, probably by antiaircraft ground fire. As a result of the second incident, heated tension erupted between Rangoon and the White House. The Burmese government strongly condemned American clandestine air missions aimed at providing aid and support to separatist ethnic minorities who took refuge in the deep jungle of northern Burma. Once again the United States was caught in an embarrassing position and did not know how best to deal with the matter. To satisfy Rangoon's demand for a public apology was something that the American Department of State could easily do, but such action would be tantamount to an official acknowledgment of Washington's plotting to overthrow the legitimate government of Burma, and the consequences of such an admission on the diplomatic front were imponderable.

This piece of news about the Air America disaster was a very small item lost among all the reports of many national events. But to a journalist of my inclination, it was valuable as a meaningful confirmation of the story of the Green Belt, a strategic defensive belt of territory designed to keep the mainland Chinese out of Southeast Asia. Gradually, I came to have a fairly accurate view of the importance of events in the highlands in the larger context of international relations. With that understanding, I believed I would be able to avoid excited and emotional responses when venturing into a search for the significance of new events.

The war caused bloodshed in the highlands, burned a swath across the countryside, and led to disturbing demonstrations all over the city of Saigon. But if one was a member of *la Haute Société,* the upper echelon of society, one would still be able to find quiet places to relax. After having slept in the whole morning, Davis arranged to meet me for lunch at the *Cercle Sportif.* Though I did not belong to the bourgeois class who patronized this sports facility, I still came here now and then because of the need to establish and maintain contacts essential to my job. The water in the club's swimming pool was clear and blue as ever, and its grounds were blessed with cool shadows cast by tall trees. At this time of day, few Vietnamese were around. The sun was very hot and bright, and no breeze was felt. Even so, a few scantily clad young women were sunbathing, their skin tanned to a dark shade of bronze. Davis and I chose a table near the edge of the pool. Occasionally, we had to close our eyes against blobs of sunlight reflecting from the rippling surface of the water.

A sexy young woman stepped out of the pool, followed by a hairy-chested American man. Davis recognized Tacelosky before I did, but coolly showed no sign of recognition.

"That guy Tacelosky is a curious specimen," Davis said to me in a low voice. "This is not only because whenever and wherever you meet him, you see him with a new woman. Rather, it's the legend of his life: three times having parachuted into North Vietnam; three times having returned intact. No one else is fated to survive better than he. When it comes to knowledge of Asian mountains and jungles and ethnic groups here in Vietnam, he has no equal. He will be a dangerous adversary if you choose to oppose him. He has caused so much difficulty for General Thuyet."

I remembered something and asked Davis about it. "Is he one of the two persons who were deported at the same time in 1963 by the Diem government, the other being the journalist Martin?"

"The exact same person," Davis replied. "After being thrown out of Vietnam, he was sent to Vientiane, specifically tasked with organizing, in Upper Laos and Northeastern Thailand, units of Hmong fighters. These well-trained combatants effectively limited infiltration of communist soldiers from North Vietnam down the Ho Chi Minh Trail. Their area of operation is considered the most formidable section of the Green Belt. It's too bad for Tacelosky that when he returned to the Central Highlands, he no longer had full authority to do what he pleased, and therefore he has carried a grudge against General Thuyet ever since."

Davis proceeded to elaborate on Tacelosky's background. Originally sent to Vietnam from Fort Bragg, Tacelosky was now a retired Special Forces lieutenant colonel, at present ostensibly chief representative of the USAID office responsible for the highlands. It was common knowledge that Fort Bragg is the primary location where the Green Berets are trained before being sent to the faraway corners of the world, be those corners the thick jungles of Africa or the isolated coastal areas of Latin America. But, at present, their major operational area was Southeast Asia, where multiple ethnic minorities are scattered over high mountains and green jungles stretching from the eastern seaboard to near the foot of the Himalayas. Into each country, Special Forces overtly or secretly sent its special operations troops who, being well acquainted with local customs and languages by virtue of their elaborate training, adapted themselves quickly to the local scene and helped local people improve their lives as a way of winning their hearts and minds.

Subsequently, the responsibility of Special Forces soldiers was to do their best to organize units of local combatants, ensuring that they were well-trained, malleable, and under reliable command of American officers. Their current great ambition was to establish a well-controlled, solid Green Belt of jungle terrain that they believed efficacious in fighting against all forms of communist guerrilla warfare. One could say that this strategic operation was a semi-official experimental project of both the CIA and the Special Forces, which Washington and the Pentagon had not acknowledged as such. In truth, Special Forces soldiers were the president's cherished children who enjoyed preferential treatment and unlimited privileges, but that would not stop them from becoming illegitimate unrecognized children when their secret mission was exposed. Evidence of their activities was found in the recent rebellions in the highlands, and now in Air America's mishaps in Laos and Burma. In addition, the international press often exposed subversive activities of Special Forces against existing legitimate governments of allied countries.

"Coming from Eastern Europe, Tacelosky became a naturalized American after the Second World War," Davis added, returning to the individual under discussion. "He has lived in Asia, especially Vietnam, for many years, and has gained a lot of experience dealing with communist guerrillas. After many tours of duty, he went back to America only soon to volunteer to return again to Vietnam. Though he rarely comes to Saigon, he keeps a room at the Continental Hotel; whenever he is in town, he never fails to appear at this place around noontime. Besides his excellent skills as a sharpshooter and in wielding a knife for lethal purposes, he is also a good tennis player—and with a billiard cue, he's a person to be reckoned with. In addition, he is known for cruelty toward his women."

Tacelosky emerged from the room where one changed clothes after swimming, his face directed toward where Davis and I sat. The man was big and snuggly outfitted in a white short-sleeved shirt and light slacks. His face had grown crimson red from the sun and from plenty of alcohol. He rushed over to our table and gave Davis's shoulder a hard punch as Davis stood in greeting.

"Hey," Tacelosky addressed Davis, his voice loud and familiar, "I've thought you'd gone off to Djakarta a long time ago. How come Martin in Hong Kong told me that?"

The two of them standing side by side were a study in contrasts. Davis confirmed that he would be going to the capital of Indonesia at the beginning of the following week.

At that moment, Tacelosky's companion came out of the changing room, her straight and long legs moving on light steps. Instead of verbal greetings, she merely smiled, her eyes all the while warmly responding to the hot desirous looks thrown at her from around the pool. It was to me very unsightly for a woman to pull out a chair for herself while accompanied by a Western man, which was exactly what this woman did at that moment. Tacelosky did not seem to care about this, and virtually ignored her presence. Coolly, he talked with Davis in French, his heavy accent bearing a trace of German. He presented a smart appearance. The thick skin of his face marked with big pores made no great impression. But to compensate for that, his heavy thick lips betrayed a sensual lust, and they were set off by a dandy vulgar moustache. Unconcerned for common propriety, Tacelosky pulled up a chair for himself and sat with us without invitation. He ordered more food and drinks. As usual, I only asked for a glass of cognac diluted with soda. Davis preferred wine, and Tacelosky indulged himself immoderately with whiskey, as though it was only water.

"Minister and Mrs. Denman asked about you, Davis," Tacelosky began. "The minister received your book. It seems he doesn't agree with you on many points, especially with your viewpoint on highlands issues. As for a bastard like General Thuyet, you can't talk to him about promises and morality. I'm sure you know that he's just dissolved a few CIDG camps manned by Montagnard people, camps which were operating under the direction of a Special Forces B-Team located near Da Nang; and then incorporated these camps into the Ruff-Puffs, uh, the RF-PF, the Regional Forces–Popular Forces. But the 'Yards in these camps did not accept that, and almost all of them deserted. If we hadn't found a covert way to help them out, these tribals would all have become 'Yard communists.

"What is it that makes Saigon hesitate to kick out once and for all a general who is incompetent, ignorant, and as arrogant as a feudal mandarin? His loudmouthed anticommunism is but a cover for his unrivaled corruption; all aid resources handled through him disappear without a trace, never reaching the 'Yards. Troops and tanks under his command haven't been seen engaged in military operations even once. All of them stay in the city to guard and protect his headquarters, making it as strong and secure as a medieval fortress. Added to that, he's also found various ways to cause difficulty for American soldiers, even for Minister Denman. Fortunately, he was thrown out of the Central Highlands and dispatched to I Corps, where, if not the Buddhists, then the communists will destroy him."

I had not expected that Tacelosky would be so abusive toward General Thuyet. Davis, in my presence, appeared embarrassed by the kind of language used by his compatriot.

In his typical adopted Eastern calmness and humor, Davis said, "Well, General Thuyet will not be destroyed, as his fame and power are on the rise, and there is hope that he will become president."

Davis's words aroused a furor in Tacelosky. "If that is to be the case," the man retorted, face getting redder, "we Americans should sign the South over to the communists right now, so we don't squander more young American blood or waste energy in a useless fight."

Davis addressed his response to Tacelosky as if the thought had just came to him. "Incidentally, it's curious that I have not heard from any American official, including Minister Denman, a single good comment about their Vietnamese allies in the highlands. The target of their most intense criticism has been General Thuyet and his subordinates. Yet, as for General Tri, who has replaced General Thuyet, the situation appears to be quite different."

"Do you know," asked Tacelosky facetiously, in ready reply, "only incompetent corrupt people from all over the country have been sent to work in the highlands? This is an administrative measure: these elements are sent into internal exile in lieu of penalties given out by law courts. Only recently have I come to understand why our aid program has failed after being handled for many months by such elements. They're really a lazy bunch which knows nothing other than stealing and betraying—unlike the 'Yards, who are ignorant, but subservient and simple.

"As I see it, in Asia, corruption has become an enduring and incorrigible tradition. If the Americans do not take upon themselves to assume all responsibility and a leading role, in no time at all this country will fall into communist hands. When will the Embassy and our American generals begin to realize the uselessness of their agreements with the GVN and their pledges to

Saigon in the midst of having to confront the present difficulties of unconventional guerrilla warfare? Given the strategic importance of a region like the Central Highlands, the Tri-Border Area, which is a springboard for infiltration into the Mekong delta and across to the coast, its security, and the authority to manage it, must be entrusted completely to us. I'm definitely sure that a mountainous region without the Vietnamese presence, managed exclusively by the Montagnards and the Green Berets, will no longer see in it a single communist."

From his language and personality, one could easily see projected the true nature of a white adventurer of the nineteenth century. Tacelosky was, indeed, a person with a lot of dangerous tricks up his sleeve, a fact that he took no care to conceal. Davis realized that the man was a catalyst for change in the present situation, and his presence in the highlands surely would lead to new arrangements and new events.

"Damn it," Tacelosky continued, "we merely play an advisory role, but we have to bear the consequences of the advisee's failure. Certainly we can't accept such terms of service. Moreover, the honor of the U.S. Army and of America is tied to what happens here. We can't afford failure and defeat. Those two words don't exist in Green Beret vocabulary."

The man kept on filling his glass with alcohol and emptying it in single gulps. His woman tried to restrain him by coyly removing the still-full glass from his clasping hand. Tacelosky embraced her and leaned down to give her a deep kiss on the lips. The woman accepted it, with a perfunctory gesture of protest. He showed his notice of my presence when he turned to the subject of painting.

"Look," he said to Davis, "if your friend wanted to paint a nude figure, I would guarantee that this woman has a perfectly beautiful body for that purpose."

The woman blushed with embarrassment at this impudent observation. Tacelosky said to her: "Are you not proud of your beauty?"

Then, turning to us, he proceeded like an experienced playboy to explain his preference for Asian women. "The attraction of Asian women lies perhaps in their inherent shyness. It's not as though I can't see beauty in American women, but I find that women here have an exciting and unusual appeal."

Davis commented in good-humored manner that such unusualness was a projection of Tacelosky's preference for variety, or of his exotic taste.

Unexpectedly, Tacelosky dropped his playful talk and turned to challenge Davis. "Now, how will you American journalists write about these ungrateful people who are ready to beg for money from us, but still hold demonstrations against us, burn our cars, demand peace, and want to kick us out of here and back to America? Fuck the peaceniks is what I say! The American leadership has never before been this weak, not daring to commit themselves all the way to a war long in progress. Their present attempts to inculcate a so-called democracy here shows that they know absolutely nothing about the traditional way of ruling society practiced in Asia. People here can only be ruled by force and severe punishment. Those Chinese emperors whose reigns lasted for long periods knew this fact well. The current policy of Mao Tse-tung, which follows this philosophy of force, is but a variant."

Given the existence of the likes of Tacelosky, I now appreciated the reason for General Thuyet's fury—and his responses, which could be seen as unreasonable and extremist. It was in the general's nature not to tolerate excessive demands, even when they came from the students in Hue.

I excused myself, leaving Davis with Tacelosky's rant.

In the evening, the writer-advisor to General Thuyet drove to my paper's office to pick me up. He told me that General Thuyet wanted to meet me because he thought well of the newspaper articles I wrote about the highlands. In turn, I mentioned the excellent speech the general had delivered on the radio the day before, and praised it as an extraordinary feat of language. For the first time, the writer did not seem honored by the compliment. He declared that trifling skills in language were not what made good works of literature, that what was important was a fiery ardor in writing, which existed only in the younger generation.

"To tell you the truth," he continued, "it was the brain trust that wrote the speech for the general, whereas my contribution was no more than a few suggestions." There was a sigh. "You wait and see, these youngsters are very good," he proudly observed. "Only they have been greatly influenced by the American type of democracy."

This brought to mind copies of an underground paper that came to my newspaper's office through the regular postal service, without any indication of where they had came from. I agreed with the writer about the American influence on the younger generation. As if on cue, at this point VOA ended their evening news report and, right after a piece of music between programs, presented an interview with several Vietnamese student leaders who were presently in Washington, D.C. Four of Dr. Ross's students had arrived in America to begin a long journey across various states and to many university campuses. As usual, one again heard their familiar forceful voice defending American intervention into the war in South Vietnam, and approving acceleration of the bombing of North Vietnam. I switched channels to the evening music program of an FM station.

"When did they go to America? Why did I hear nothing about this?" the writer asked me, puzzled.

"A few days ago, I saw them with Dr. Ross at the Information Bureau," I replied. "Nothing goes on without his involvement."

"Professor Ross is a very close friend of General Thuyet, but there seems to have been some fissure between them resulting from their disagreement on the highlands issue. Incidentally, I hear that Dr. Ross will be sending three Thuong students to America to study for five years, without it being necessary to acquire approval from the government committee in charge of overseas education."

"He holds no official position and role," I observed to the writer, "but, as I said, nothing seems to transpire without passing through his hands."

The writer was deep in thought behind the steering wheel. "I think President Diem was courageous and sensible when dealing firmly with Dr. Ross, especially after his involvement with disturbances in the highlands in the early '60s."

The section of road immediately leading to the general's private residence in Saigon was barricaded, strung with barbed wire, and guarded by soldiers. The writer slowed to a stop. A paratrooper bent down and looked into the car. Recognizing the writer, he politely saluted and gestured for the car to move on. This brought to mind the criticism that Tacelosky had earlier in the day directed toward General Thuyet's behavior while he was still in command of the highlands, and which I had also seen in the American press: that the general's headquarters always looked like a strong fortress protected by the best of military means. This might also be true to a lesser extent with regard to his private residence in the capital. The mansion was very posh, separated from the outside world by bamboo latticework and high hedges formed of broadleaf evergreen trees with interlaced branches.

The general was today seen in civilian attire. He was stripped of the fierce appearance of a military officer, and suggested instead the image of a tame tiger without his stripes. He was happy to see the writer. Pleasantly, he shook my hands and praised me for the constructive ideas in my newspaper articles.

"The situation of the country is gradually improving," he informed me. "I have given orders to ease pressure on struggle movements, especially in Hue. To begin with, this morning the Police Field Force unit withdrew and returned to Da Nang. I am also asking the government to end the protective measures applied to monk Pháp Viên, provided that he does not return to Hue."

Then, in the next breath, the general took pains to justify what he had done in response to the Buddhist struggle in Hue. He maintained that in the position of representing the government, it was his responsibility to restore public order and security, but his deep aspiration was still progress toward a true democratic regime. With regard to monk Pháp Viên in particular, the general admired and respected him, but being pressured by the central government, the general could not do anything differently.

Here in the general's residence, I met again the lieutenant colonel in charge of the II Corps Tactical Zone's Psychological Warfare Bureau, and Major Y Ksor, both having just arrived from the highlands. It was clear that General Thuyet still had a hold on his former subordinates.

The general turned to Y Ksor and announced: "I am applying pressure to suggest that the central government raise the Bureau of Highlands Affairs to the rank of a ministry like any other ministry in the government. And perhaps you, yourself, Major Y Ksor, will take the responsibility for that ministry."

Y Ksor could only bow his head in submission.

As he turned toward the colonel, the general's voice took on an exasperated tone. "And now, Colonel, how are your people doing their jobs up there so that the communists are so often allowed to rob buses and kill passengers? And what is the truth behind this business of Thuong Local Forces killing two

Vietnamese soldiers before the whole company fled to Cambodia with their weapons? What in the world is General Tri doing?"

The colonel confirmed the news and explained that the problem originated with the Thuong who were elements of the Civilian Irregular Defense Group, CIDG, those Thuong fostered by the American Green Berets.

General Thuyet could not hold back his fury. "Already, two years ago, I warned the government about this, saying that all those Thuong groups had to be dissolved so we would have a military force unified under one command, the Vietnamese high command."

His angry eyes glaring, the general dismissed the two officers after having arranged to see them again the following day before they returned to the highlands. After they left, the general's facial expression noticeably softened. Cannily, the writer chose this moment to mention positive public response to the speech the general had given on the radio. The general laughed and forgot all about his troubled feelings of a few moments earlier. The dining table was set for twelve people. On the right of the general sat the writer, with myself next in line. The remaining people were all very young and the core members of the general's advisory staff. Besides the inevitable presence of the law professor, there counted among them a naval lieutenant commander, two captains from the Joint General Staff, a Ph.D. in the social sciences, a journalist, two experts in repatriating displaced villagers back to pacified villages, and, notably, a student leader.

The general displayed an agreeable and easygoing manner toward us. The young people, not suffering from self-consciousness, conversed rather freely. The sociologist talked about the necessity of incorporating social justice into the government's agenda for revolution in society. The journalist offered a very sound assessment of the insecurity felt by the masses when they experienced themselves losing their identity, a sense of which served to confirm their existence and their presence among others. In his turn, the young naval officer touched upon the philosophy of military revolution as exemplified by the experience of Nasser in the Middle East, wherein each soldier of the future was to be at the same time a political worker, an educator, or an agriculturist. As might be expected, the student leader strongly criticized the current educational system and demanded reform for universities, with a view to establishing new standards of value. Discussion and debate on all these issues were directed to the general's attention, by way of making him aware that it was time leadership must be handed over to the younger generation, if one wanted to have a modernized society in the future.

CHAPTER SIXTEEN

It was a day like any other day, a day I was to be on time at the newspaper's office so as to work on the layout of news items for the front page, which would go to press in the afternoon. But I arose late, probably because of the heavy dose of alcohol consumed at General Thuyet's residence the night before. I did not go straight up to my office, but stopped by the small shop selling refreshments at the entrance to the alley. I recognized the same familiar grimy faces of printing shop workers and machinists. Also present was the disabled soldier who had lost his legs. They discussed impending demonstrations and various strategies considered by the Buddhist leadership. The name of Pháp Viên came up often, accompanied by contradictory comments about him. Eventually, the conversation shifted to the explosion at one of the hotels built especially for richer American clientele, a hotel located in Cholon, the vibrant commercial area of the Saigon municipality inhabited mostly by Chinese. The deafening early morning explosion had rocked many surrounding streets.

A machinist directed his gaze toward the high-rise building across the street. "As long as the Americans live in that building, chances are we here will get the brunt of a bomb attack," he observed.

His words did not sit well with Miss Tam, owner of the shop, whose superstitious beliefs decried his ominous tongue. Rather piqued, she whirled around to walk toward the back of the shop, her skin-tight nylon blouse revealing the allure of flesh and curves, so much so that a writer sitting there proclaimed that they were a live petition. The sexual drive was usually activated in me only when my body was tired. I had gone to sleep late last night and now my head was a little groggy.

Sluggishly, I walked up to the paper's office. As soon as he saw my face, the editor started to nag. "Where in the world were you the whole of last night?"

He must have thought that I had not returned home at all last night. Whatever the insinuation, his question was not proper. I recognized a sharp edge in my voice even as I tried to reply calmly.

"I slept in my home as usual. Yesterday morning I attended the press conference at the Joint General Staff compound, then in the evening I had dinner at General Thuyet's residence. Why, was something wrong?"

From the way the secretary regarded me, and from the anxious look in the editor's eyes, I had a premonition that something out of the ordinary was about to happen. Could this have something to do with the possibility of the paper being shut down? That was the only very important issue which could weigh upon the fate of many people at the paper. It was a Damoclean sword hung by a single hair that at any time could drop and chop us off at the neck.

"Have we been served with another warning about having our paper closed down?" I asked the editor.

"No, that's not it. Actually we can consider that threat gone for now. Let me ask you truthfully: besides working as a journalist, are you engaged in any other kind of activities?"

"Yes, previously I painted, and right now once in a while I still do. But you already know that. Why do you have to ask again?"

Without further utterance, but with an expression akin to commiseration, the editor handed me an official summons affixed with a bright red seal. I was completely stunned for a minute, but pulled myself together soon afterwards. It was a notification from the Military Security Service specifically instructing me to immediately present myself, the purpose of which would later be revealed to me. For a moment, I recalled my relationships with various people and thought over all I had worked on, but I could not identify any reason that might lead to the interest the MSS had in talking with me. The secretary informed me that early in the morning two jeeps, bearing false license plates, brought plain-clothed security agents who rushed into the office to look for me. Not finding me, they recorded statements from all employees and wrote down relevant addresses, then requested that the editor try by all means to contact me.

The editor displayed great anxiety and concern for me in face of this new development. Then, considerately, and in the voice of one who had experienced much in life, he solicitously talked to me: "Try to remember and consider clearly all your connections and associations, and see if you have, in some measure, allied yourself with someone politically. As I see it, this is some serious issue above and beyond a journalistic matter. I am sure they have posted their people to keep your place under surveillance. That you have not been detained by them by now is pure luck. I suggest that you stay hidden somewhere and wait for me to find out the reason for this summons before you reappear. Once you are taken by them, it will be very difficult to find a way to get you free."

I considered his advice and conjectured that what I had written about the highlands was the root of my trouble. Meanwhile, seeing the editor's extreme agitation, I felt obliged to calm him down. I firmly assured him that none of my activities was illegal to the extent that it could land me in jail. As for contacts and relations, as a journalist I had the right to meet anyone, from a priest to a monk, from military leaders to anti-government elements; and that could not be conceived of as a crime. I, myself, felt less anxious when considering that it was preferable to appear publicly before the general who was the director of the Military Security Service, rather than to be arrested in the shadows by his violent and irresponsible underlings.

Upon this thought, I calmly decided that I would present myself right away, agreeing with the office's staff that if I did not return after six hours it would mean that I had been arrested. I also asked the secretary to give Như Nguyện a call and inform her that I would go to Hue tomorrow—as if things were in their normal order. I truly did not want her to worry about me in relation to such unknown troubles as suggested by this incident. It was rather surprising that at this moment of vulnerability my only thought was of Như Nguyện.

In the afternoon, to the delight of the editor and my fellow employees, I returned to the newspaper's office. My guesswork had turned out to be incorrect, because the reason for the summons was not my writing about the highlands problem. Rather, it resulted from the five-thousand-word interview article on monk Pháp Viên which I had allowed Davis to use. The monk's criticism of the military, as recorded in that article, had aroused anger from several generals, which led to my meeting with the general who was the director of the MSS—a meeting conducted in an atmosphere fraught with warning and threat.

The MSS general had been promoted to his present rank thanks to his success in suppressing the Buddhist movement in

Hue. After I had been shown in, he threw down on the glass surface of his desk a complete photocopy of the teletyped article that had been sent from Davis's office. I noted that on the same desktop lay a Smith and Wesson pistol, and beside it a stubby grenade launcher holding down stacks of brand-new U.S. dollars. Now firm, now flexible were his words to me; but in the main his accusations were vague, ill-founded. He accused the press of having stabbed the military in the back, and considered me an efficient spokesman for monk Pháp Viên. Seeing me in that role was precisely what made the general furious with me.

It was my understanding that since he was escorted to Saigon from Hue, the monk had been kept completely in isolation, as the government wanted his name to fade from the memory of the people. This was indicative of the government's lingering fear of the monk's spiritual power and influence. According to the general, what I did with my interview of monk Pháp Viên was no less than a heavy blow to the government's policy regarding him, and it could very well have affected public opinion in America. Once again, I was given guidance as to how and in what direction to do my job as a journalist, this time by the general, a man who had no expertise whatsoever in this field of activities.

The irony of this would be matched only by my offering to be a security advisor to him. On the other hand, it must be said that after a ninety-six-minute meeting with the general in charge of MSS, my prejudice toward him decreased and I liked him better. He was the rash and impulsive type, but straightforward and disposed to tell the truth even to his opponents. The tendency in me to firmly confront problems seemed to have evoked the willfulness inherent to him, so that he looked pleased, as though having found a kindred soul. He did not have the wicked brazenness that I had imagined of one in his career and position. For all that, I considered myself lucky to have entered the main door and to have met him personally.

But misfortune never comes in singlet, as declared by folk wisdom. Indeed, the next day I escaped death by just a thin line. The communists always claimed that they only targeted Americans in their attacks, but this time for sure no American was harmed, and the high-rise apartment building across the street from my paper's office still stood haughtily, completely intact. Very often, one's fate depends on a slight change of habit, like sitting leisurely in Miss Tam's shop with a cup of coffee early in the morning, which I usually did and which I neglected to do this very day.

Learning of the news of the bomb attack, a panicked Như Nguyện drove to my office to look for me, even though many streets were still barricaded. Photojournalists, like a flock of vultures, surrounded a heap of dead bodies. Như Nguyện cried with happiness upon seeing me; she embraced and kissed me passionately. Having just gone through shock, my chest heavy with pressure, I did not respond in kind.

"Are you all right?" she asked, worried. "Let me drive you home. You need to rest a few days so you can feel well enough to go to Hue with me."

I was touched. "Don't worry. I don't need to go home. I can go with you anywhere you like from now until the evening."

She changed the subject. "What did you do to be called to the Military Security Service?"

When I expressed surprise that she knew about it, Như Nguyện smiled. "There's nothing you do that I don't know about. Why did you give me that lie about going to Hue instead of the MSS? Don't you want to have me care for you?"

Her loving reproach had the effect of removing all my uncomfortable feelings about her personal life. Recently, I had heard much about her – mostly negative. Indeed, Như Nguyện was too often mentioned with much jealousy and envy. She was a necessary presence for many people, and it was pathetic that every one of the men courting her felt that she reserved special treatment for him alone. In my vision now was a gentle woman whose clear voice was that of purity. Nothing could spoil my good thoughts about Như Nguyện.

"Darling Triet, I am thinking of visiting Hue even before you start teaching there. Let's go to Hue for this coming Tet celebration. I would like to take you to Vĩ Dạ village to relive my days as a teenager in that wonderful place."

In a voice that sounded distant, she continued. "When reaching a certain age, we begin to see things slip through our fingers as if in a dream."

I told Như Nguyện that given what had just transpired, I definitely wanted to quit journalism, and perhaps would be content to move to Hue and teach at the College of Fine Arts. I needed quietude, and hoped I would be able to paint again up there.

"You don't have to worry about that. The house where I stay in Vĩ Dạ village is surrounded by a large garden and a stand of trees perched on a bank of the Perfume River. In the afternoon, all you hear is sounds of the breeze gliding over tiny waves."

This woman carried in her heart many memories of a childhood spent in her home village. I imagined a breeze rippling the surface of the river and caressing the long dark hair of a Hue girl. But the sudden thought of the disturbances transpiring in that city brought me doubt.

"You have not been back to Hue for a long while," I said. "The city has undergone many changes in the meantime. Hue is full of revolutionary struggles now. It's no longer quiet and calm as in the old days."

"I think those disturbances are only temporary, and in the main journalists tend to be attracted to noisy events only. The real face of Hue is seen elsewhere, behind edges of green plants and flowers—edges that must be discovered. It's dormant, calm, and cool, like the soul of a true Hue man."

I smiled at the thought of Như Nguyện's true Hue man.

She informed me that she had officially been recalled to the Ministry of Foreign Affairs in Saigon and probably would work as a special assistant to the minister for a while. Như Nguyện lived a carefree life and was accustomed to changes. My skylark should be able to fly high and sing its song, I reminded myself.

Như Nguyện insisted on giving me a ride home. I did not protest, but requested that we stop by Davis's office on the way. Davis was not there, and we were told that he was at the AP news agency and would return shortly.

We waited. It was in a congenial atmosphere that we greeted one another upon Davis's return. There was no indication that he knew of the latest explosion this morning, and I did not want to talk about an unpleasant experience. No introduction was required, as Davis and Như Nguyện had met each other many times at the Ministry of Foreign Affairs and were thus well-acquainted. Như Nguyện did not drink. Davis knowingly gave me a cognac and soda, while he preferred straight whiskey. His small office was cozy, the familiar map of Southeast Asia in its usual place on the pure white wall. Davis had just returned from a two-day trip to Tokyo. After all, moving about was the way of life for journalists.

Turning toward Như Nguyện, Davis said, "In Tokyo, I had dinner with the Vietnamese ambassador and asked about you. Only then did I learn that you have returned to Saigon to work as a cultural assistant at the ministry."

"There is nothing definite about that. Besides, dealing in foreign affairs, I do not wish to stay at any one place for long, especially when it is in Vietnam," she replied.

Both Davis and I laughed at her statement. The freewheeling lifestyle she chose was by no means mirrored in her face, a face that displayed the characteristics of a traditional Asian beauty.

"Oh, Triet!" Davis exclaimed. "I have just remembered: I also met Kux in Tokyo. He mentioned that you like André Malraux. So he sent you the English version of Malraux's *Anti-Memoirs* which has just been published."

Holding the book in my hands, I flipped through the pages and looked at the last one. It was my habit to begin a book by reading some of its last lines.

At that moment, Dr. Ross arrived, big and loud and bubbling with joy, like a gust of wind unexpectedly blowing in. He had not been back in the United States very long before turning around and showing up in Vietnam again. I did not know the reason that his scheduled three-month vacation was canceled. At present, he was extremely busy helping the Ministry of Education promote the program called "Youth and Students for the Countryside." It was a summer activity aimed at sending students and other youths to rural areas to offer social services, the ultimate political purpose of which was to neutralize the opposition tendency among this younger generation by, essentially, keeping them too busy to think of causing unrest.

While casually extracting for himself a bottle of beer from a small refrigerator, Ross abruptly broached the subject of a seemingly new discovery. "I must admit that the protection system in apartment buildings built for Americans is absolutely superb. Only when witnessing the explosion this morning did I realize well that fact."

Davis hastily inquired, "What explosion? A new one? Where? Being in this air-conditioned room, I could only have felt the windows rattle."

"You didn't know? How could you miss the news? It happened at the biggest of apartment buildings, the one recently built on Pham Ngu Lao Street. The remarkable thing is that no American was injured, even when the blast was caused by suicide attackers strapped with some dozens of kilograms of plastic explosive."

Như Nguyện looked surprised when I said nothing. Hearing the street name mentioned, Davis turned to question me. "Triet, if I am not mistaken, your newspaper's office is on that same street. Don't you know anything about it either?"

"Well, actually, it happened right across the street from my office. I was on the phone at that moment, and the impact of the blast threw me off the chair. I felt chest pain caused by the pressure wave and suffered some cuts from the broken glass fragments."

The ensuing conversation centered upon details of damage, followed by speculation and hypotheses. Looking through transparent glass window panes, Ross said to Davis in a reprimanding voice, "I've told you many times to have someone secure those glass panes with tape. Even distant explosions can become dangerous when you don't take care of little things like that."

Davis cracked a wisp of a smile, the smile seen on a calm person who has experienced plenty of exposure to dangerous mishaps. "Real threat to this fifth floor comes only when the communists resort to using rockets."

We all laughed, casual and calm. War-related accidents had become too much an ordinary part of life to deserve much attention from anyone.

Davis asked Ross about the progress made by Vietnamese students in their mission of neutralizing the antiwar movement raging on American university campuses.

His voice full of enthusiasm, Ross replied happily. "Tremendous success! I didn't expect that they could be that good. They had a bit of a rough time initially when they were suspected of being sent by the Vietnamese government. But after that, things have been running smoothly, wheels turning on axle grease. As you all know, university professors and students, like the rest of the American people, don't know anything to speak of about the situation here. Therefore, American public opinion has to be reshaped. I'm planning to arrange for the students to make a tour of Europe after the U.S. That's also a way of rewarding them for their efforts."

I expressed interest in knowing how the three Thuong students were doing, those who had been sponsored by Ross to pursue their higher education in America.

"They're not college students yet," Ross replied. "They've just finished high school, and were Dr. Denman's students. The minister was afraid that they would quit school and escape to the jungle to join the separatist movement, so he wanted to send them to America. The fact is: most Thuong students want to drop out and enlist in a Mike Force, a special assault group and reaction team recruited, armed, provisioned, and commanded by American Special Forces personnel—or to go into Cambodia and join the separatists."

He stopped to consider the matter, then in a thoughtful tone reiterated Minister Denman's viewpoint. "Return to Caesar what belongs to Caesar. I'm afraid that giving back the right of self-government to ethnic minorities is something inevitable. The important point is: one should not waste any more flesh and blood."

Elsewhere, Ross had again and again mentioned that inevitability, or in his words, *The Inevitable Day*. He observed that Vietnamese often showed they were very sensitive about the racial issue, but for some unknown reason they were not conscious of the unavoidable reality that would and must happen.

Davis shifted the subject to Ross's present residence after his journey to America. "Listen, do you still live in the villa on Duy Tan Street? I visited it once and met no one but a few student leaders there."

Ross gave Davis a mischievous smile and gestured with his hand while talking. "I've just rented a very beautiful villa on Hien Vuong Street. Each of you, please do come for a visit. It is replete with a tennis court, and a pool by which one can enjoy sun-bathing. I let the young people use the Duy Tan villa as a meet-ing place, and also allow the youths from IVS, International Voluntary Services, to stay there whenever they come to Saigon to work. By the way, this afternoon I am holding a cocktail party at my new residence, to which I have invited a number of Vietnamese writers for the purpose of introducing them to the lady writer Beko, who is the new cultural attaché at the Embassy. I gather Ms. Nhu̕ Nguyện will accompany the Foreign Affairs Minister. I'd like to extend my personal invitation to our fine painter here, and to you, Davis."

Without waiting for our reply, Ross continued by asking me about two writers by the names of Dao Khiem and Ho Lam. His question triggered my memory of a rumor about an association of free writers that was to be formed in the near future through Ross's arrangement.

"You can ask me anything about painting," I replied. "As to the two writers you mentioned, I have heard their names but have not read any book written by them."

What he said next proved that Ross was very knowledgeable about many issues in many fields. Indeed, he had gathered correct and essential information on the said writers. "It appears that both of them are rather well-known," Ross proclaimed. "Ho Lam is an author of the 1940s' generation, strongly anticommunist, who highly praises the leading role of the middle class. Dao Khiem, on the other hand, is a champion of literary experiments who leads a group of young innovative writers. I regret that my Vietnamese is too limited to allow me the pleasure of reading them. But it would seem that both men are very much influenced by French culture. Is that correct?"

Since entering the field of journalism, I had acquired the virtue of tolerance for lengthy and winding dialogues, especially one in the present circumstance with Dr. Ross. I could not give him any extra, albeit firm, information on any relevant issue, as what he knew and expressed was already well-founded.

Ross continued. "I'm thinking of the absence of a research journal like *Học Tập*, 'Studies and Practice' produced in the North, in which expressed ideas come from those who engage in practical application of knowledge. But here in the South, the brain is at one place and the arm at another. The danger for us is precisely that point."

I myself was thinking of the current trend in the South of creating and advocating doctrines or philosophies related to social reform, of the book *Thoughts on the Two Revolutions* by General Thuyet—and once again recognized that Ross's observations and his concerns were not misdirected. Some time ago, in appraising Americans in Vietnam, Davis had come up with a sharp remark: the majority of them could not adapt themselves to the local scene, for they were arrogant and pompous out of ignorance, devoid of imagination and creativity. Against the background of that crowd, Ross was undoubtedly an exception, one above and beyond Davis's generalization.

The anesthetic I had been given wore off, and the stitches caused some pain. The tetanus shot began to take effect and made me feel feverish. My forehead was wet with perspiration. Như Nguyện looked at me with both loving and alarm. Ross had finished his third bottle of beer. I went to the bar and poured myself half a glass of Scotch and drank it in a gulp. I could feel the liquor run down and heat up my entire chest. Ross bid good-bye to us in order to go teach a class on international law at the university.

Davis closed the door after Ross, turned around, and exclaimed, "How can he take on so many things like that? I know that some Vietnamese senators have even sought his help in resolving difficulties within the national assembly."

"He is a super mind," I said. "He can be involved in many things at the same time without showing lack of proper attention to any of them."

Next, Davis produced a gift for me he had bought in Tokyo, a copy of the published catalog of the collection of the world's paintings acquired by President Sukarno, who, besides having a very beautiful young concubine, proved to be an experienced playboy with an artistic orientation. The collection featured old and modern paintings from around the world, from Picasso's cubism to the soft ethereal atmosphere in some selected Vietnamese paintings on silk.

"Sukarno has not seen your paintings," Davis commented, "otherwise he would have kept at least one of them for his collection."

Như Nguyện smiled at that. In my dimming consciousness, the image of her receded, becoming a luminous imprint upon the cloak of a dark, distant backdrop. I was tired, truly tired, and now wanted to plunk myself down any place and go to sleep, like on the sofa in Davis's office—had Như Nguyện not been with me.

In the dark elevator carrying the two of us down to street level, Như Nguyện pulled my head down toward her and kissed me.

"You need a rest," she said caringly. "For the rest of the day, I will not let you go anywhere. I myself will cook for you whatever you want to eat. We don't have to eat out."

Though exhausted, I wanted to make some gesture to express my appreciation for her care. I placed a light kiss on her fragrant hair—a gesture saying many words, as silent as in a dream. I had the intention of painting her, capturing the fleeting image that had presented itself to my mind's eye only a moment ago, the image of an enlivened brilliant face on a dense sepia background.

Như Nguyện stayed with me for the rest of the day. The woman's skill in tidying up my many things brought a changed cozy atmosphere to the front room. Sweet gentle notes of music served as a backdrop for her crystal-clear words and laughter. She did not go to the reception for writers at Ross's residence. We also canceled our dinner appointment with Davis. All we consumed for dinner was soup and fruit juice.

Như Nguyện tried to lull me to sleep. She lay beside me reading until midnight. I attempted to resist the force of exhaustion that rendered me dead to the world, but sleep came nonetheless in the form of a pleasant dream: a cock's crow greeting the dawn; a few notes of birdsong trembling tree leaves; sunlight sprinkled with a powdering of dust pouring poetically through the window; tears, and a cheerful voice enfolding hope. Happiness could be as simple as the sweet near awakening from exhaustion when your woman kissed you in your dreams.

CHAPTER SEVENTEEN

Ever since I learned of the possibility that General Thuyet would return to the highlands, I decided not to let slip any opportunity to meet with him again, so as to find out more about him. As everyone knew, after the military overhaul, the general had returned to the Da Nang–Hue area as a hero, where he made another dramatic step and was successful with it: by his order, all CIDG camps, operating under the direction of the American Special Forces B-Team located near Da Nang, were formally incorporated into the Regional Forces–Popular Forces—not without a great deal of difficulty in securing logistical support, because of opposition from the Americans' MACV.

During my last meeting with him in Saigon, the general could not hide his pride and happiness when I mentioned that public opinion considered him a necessary element for stability of the highlands. He expressed a desire, perhaps eagerness, to return to the mountainous region when someone could replace him as commander of the border area, I Corps; but at the same time, he felt depressed at the thought of his own irreplaceability. The Americans realized that, at present, he was the only person who could hold the lowlands of central Vietnam, and the greatest achievement he could boast was having brought about a conciliating attitude on the part of the Buddhists.

In spite of that, however, a few days earlier in Saigon a rumor was heard that there were signs of unrest again in Hue. Seeing that this was a golden opportunity to witness the way General Thuyet operated, I accompanied the government delegation to Hue in anticipation of renewed turmoil in that city. At the same time, I tended to believe in Dr. Ross's assessment that it was hard to see how the people of Hue could return to protest and agitation after the departure of monk Pháp Viên, the soul of all struggles there.

Viewed among clouds from an airplane, Hue is an isolated island set against the Truong Son mountain range, or Annamite Cordillera, which is ragged with rocks, foliage, and stones. The city itself is enclosed by a few very gentle low mountains, and its appearance is further softened by the slowly flowing, glasslike water of the Perfume River. It was a place from which the Nguyen dynasty had ruled the country without much glory for about 150 years. Hue had been an ill-chosen location for a capital, which presented much difficulty in terms of transportation. In short, besides its historical relics, it was a city without a future, without any value in military strategy, and without any economic potential, a city which, out of self-esteem, many local people had dressed up in the brocade gown of culture.

Universities mushroomed. The city could boast only civil servants and students. In fact, the number of students had multiplied tremendously, and their choice of studying right in their hometown had rendered congested the academic environment. Culture was a responsibility far too tiresome and time consuming to work consistently upon, while the immediate impact of the war made the students lose their patience. It took them only a short step to move from quiet cultural undertakings to lively revolutionary activities, from tranquil lecture halls down noisy streets shouting and yelling in a show of the spirit of protest—with a lesser degree of responsibility than that required in works of culture.

The Cessna landed smoothly midway down the narrow runway. At the far end of the field was seen an old moss-covered citadel wall separating the airport from its urban environs. Our car took us away from the restricted military zone of the city. After that, I got out and walked on my own toward the heart of Hue.

The quietude around me was deeply palpable. A breeze wafted the subtle fragrance of lotus flowers blooming in Tịnh Tâm lake, "Lake of the Serene Heart" located within the Imperial Citadel. In the glorious days of a former life, this lake and its flowers had been meticulously taken care of to be viewed by the Nguyen emperors from their royal boat. The flowers' fragrance blended itself with the scent of burned sandalwood and joss sticks emanating from quiet small temples. Like the Buddhist philosophy of peace and harmony, the dark quiet atmosphere of Hue was not a suitable home for extremist protest movements.

Quite a big gap could be discerned between the reality of Hue and the news about it, which the press tended to blow out of all proportion. After many weeks of what was called struggle, Hue displayed nothing remarkably unusual in the demeanor of its daily life, save for banners bearing slogans hung and pasted here and there, and for painted words still legible on walls calling for a school and market boycott. Students at Đồng Khánh High School for girls had gone back to their classes as usual, displaying their shoulder-length raven hair and wearing the white *áo dài* uniform. At a crossroads, a traffic policeman waited in anticipation, hoping to see enough cars on the road to give him a chance to perform his job of directing them. American marines were busy unloading boxes of foodstuff and ammunition from their

LST, Landing Ship Tank, onto the dock dubbed *bến Tòa Khâm*, "landing by the French Resident Superior's residence." During French times, local people had used that mansion as the landmark to name the landing area across the street from it, and the name had stuck, even though at present the University of Hue stood where the residence had been. Children came around and played with the American soldiers. That was all one could see as evidence of what the press dubbed days of blood and fire.

The first place I went was the post office, where I sent a cable to my paper's office, and where I ran into Vy, an old acquaintance. Being an omnipresent person in all types of protest movements, he looked thinner and paler after having been released from detention. With the same old expression of misery on his face and a touch of sadness in his bright eyes I had seen before, Vy warmly greeted me. He supposed that I had just come from Da Nang together with General Thuyet's delegation. I only smiled a nonanswer and asked him instead about the Congress of the Youth and Students' Struggle Movement in Central Vietnam to be held the next day. Vy taught at Khải Định High School for boys. At the same time, he attempted to prolong a student's life by hanging on to a Ph.D. dissertation yet to be completed on *hát bội,* "Vietnamese classical opera." Though he seldom wrote poetry, Vy was a real poet. One of his poems had been set to music, resulting in a ballad throbbing with emotion. Disposed to social protests, while endowed with a richly artistic soul, Vy viewed revolution through the prism of pre–Second World War Vietnamese romanticism, rather than by contemplating it in the reality of the present.

"What do you think of General Thuyet?" Vy all of a sudden asked.

It was the same question I myself wanted to pose to those in the camp of protestors. Not knowing for certain the purpose of his query, I gave Vy a half answer, then presented him with another issue.

"I only know a little about General Thuyet when he was still in command of the highlands," I replied. "In the military, he is a talented general. But I don't really know for certain how he fares in other areas. Judging from his manner of resolving problems with ethnic minorities and dealing with the Americans, I would say that he is tough, but politically less than astute. Anyway, I heard that recently the general has acquired more advisors, is that right?"

Vy concurred with some part of my opinion, even as he brought up contradictory views regarding General Thuyet.

"What makes the general better than the rest of that bunch of generals," said Vy, "is that he displays a patriotic nationalist spirit and a love for revolution. The people, and even Buddhist masters, have accepted him partly on that ground. The only problem is, the general is indecisive, wavers in his position vis-à-vis the central government, and so, inevitably, we have reservations about him. As of now, the students are rather sympathetic to him, and I am sure you know that they have invited him to give a speech at their Congress tomorrow."

I accompanied Vy to the city radio station. Along the way, I noticed that Vy joined his hands together and bowed deeply in reverence to an old monk sitting in a passing cyclo. This triggered some puzzlement in the back of my mind.

"About monk Pháp Viên," I turned to ask Vy, "is there any truth in the rumors we see in the press related to him?"

"They are not exactly incorrect," Vy offered. "But each person gathered only one or two details about him, attempted to blow them up like a balloon, then attributed the modified traits to the master's personality. The real truth is that he remains simply a Zen master with the soul of an artist."

Vy further elaborated on his own knowledge of and thoughts about the person of superior monk Pháp Viên. According to him, the master had great influence on the Buddhist laity, but he declined to mix with the crowd, preferring instead to be left alone in a quiet peaceful life. While proving excellent in theology and ancient languages, he was no less passionate about playing chess and with painstakingly producing beautiful and elegant calligraphy. Though having renounced the world, monk Pháp Viên was very much attached to life. He was known for his sharp assessment of the social situation, and his opinion often had impact on political circles, especially on the opposition side.

"All kinds of people," Vy continued, "including General Thuyet, wish to meet with the master in order to secure his support. But rarely has anyone had that wish fulfilled. The master by nature is very liberal, and he doesn't like to give preferential treatment to anyone."

Vy led me inside the radio station where student leaders and members of the committee in charge of the protest movement were busy going about their tasks. Heaps of newspapers and data sheets lay in utter confusion on a large rectangular table. All ideologies found free outlet here: capitalism, Marxism, nationalism, Buddhist philosophy. What had been absorbed from published material, including new ideas and discoveries, was openly discussed. The radio station had long been controlled mainly by the students. The atmosphere surrounding their activities was pregnant with enthusiasm and revolutionary fervor. Written pieces were perfunctorily edited before broadcast, resulting in presentation of quite contradictory statements originating from the same perspective. One wondered how the Saigon authorities could judge these protestors and their activities when operating conditions of the two sides were so disparate. And this was but one among the many circumstances which were difficult for General Thuyet to deal with, as he could not clarify or explain how things evolved in his area of control. I pointed this out to Vy. Seemingly aware of the dilemma, he expressed a middle-of-the-road viewpoint.

"You know," he said rather apologetically, "the main issue is for the two sides not to push each other against the wall. I myself have warned those in the committee. But most of them are too young and too eager to listen, and it's hard to tell them not to proceed with their chosen actions."

I stayed and talked with them all until late in the afternoon when, upon Vy's suggestion, I followed him to the Perfume River where we swam. After dark, we proceeded to Vy's house in the company of a musician who was well known for his folk songs. The house, an old structure of traditional design composed of three compartments, stood amidst a garden covered in knee-high weeds. The inside of it had grown dark since sunset, for it was not supplied with electricity. In fact, even the most basic utilities normally expected in a civilized society were absent.

Aside from books and other types of publications, Vy possessed nothing to indicate that he was moving with the times. I could not fathom the extent of endurance which enabled him to live contentedly with the hushed sounds of insects and grass, by the side of an equally quiet river. It was only nine o'clock, but I had the impression that midnight had arrived. We stayed up and talked until four-thirty in the morning. During the remaining few hours of sleep, I heard far and near, at the edge of consciousness, the sound of frogs and the echo of small waves generated by a passing boat, waves sloshing against small rocks along a bank.

The next morning, at the grand playhouse in town, General Thuyet read an excellent speech to the Congress full of students. He was interrupted many times by rounds of applause that rocked the house. By discussing his philosophy of two revolutions, the general achieved the goal of evoking passion in these youths, and of reconciling inherent conflicts that had added injury to the already dismal social reality.

The general's presence would have been perfectly in accord with what his writer-advisor had planned and anticipated, had there not appeared toward the end of his speech uniforms of members of the Police Field-Force—a police unit not under control of the military commander of I Corps, the position held by the general—who arranged themselves around the playhouse. That the earlier elicited moments of goodwill and acclaim vanished instantaneously only to be replaced by an air of tense antagonism was hard to grasp, the contrast being so great. The general was furious at the way things turned out, and the students were choked with indignation. The damage to their self-respect suffered by both sides was so great as to be virtually beyond salvage. At that point, the meeting was dispersed, a fact most sadly witnessed by two of the general's advisors, the writer and the law professor. General Thuyet boarded a helicopter to return to Da Nang, and no one knew what would happen in the next few days.

It was then that I met Mr. Hoang Thai Trung. Like a shuttle, he had to rush from one to another of three universities in three cities where presently he concurrently taught: University of Saigon, University of Dalat, and University of Hue. He was now in his second week in Hue during the present period of residence. When the subject of General Thuyet's speech entered our conversation, Mr. Trung expressed his admiration for the writing style, full of spirit and the fire of its author, the writer-advisor. But at the same time he revealed his doubt as to the political role the general would fill in the future.

"How can you tell the speech was written by the writer?" I asked.

"Was there any speech delivered by the general that was not written by the writer? Moreover, as literary style is the hallmark of an accomplished author, we can be sure that such an alluring prose so full of thick vital sap could not have come from anybody else."

In this reply, I detected a subtly derisive reference to the creative applications of opium-induced hallucinations.

Mr. Trung asked me about the demonstrations going on in Saigon. He also, with much anxiety, inquired after superior monk Pháp Viên's circumstances. I told him that the monk's welfare was equally a great concern for General Thuyet, who was campaigning for the monk's release from house arrest, but there was no telling if and when that would be possible. Mr. Trung subsequently brought up the matter of my practicing journalism in Hue.

"When do you think you will finalize your decision to come here to teach?" he asked. "Perhaps together we can consider publishing a paper in this city."

"I have not given the College of Fine Arts a firm date, but perhaps it will be after Tet. I would like to be able to transfer here for a quiet atmosphere, which I need if I hope to paint again."

"Maybe everything has to begin at the beginning."

I told Mr. Trung of my plan to complete research and write a book on the highlands, elaborated from the perspective that the Thuong peoples and the Kinh people share the same roots and the same origins, a view that was entirely opposite to that of Minister Denman. Mr. Trung was in agreement with my approach and offered me encouragement.

He said, "This is a topic which I have painstakingly done research on. When teaching my students at the Faculty of Letters, I always attempt to introduce and publicize new points of view like that."

I next mentioned the suggestion by a student newspaper that an institute of research on ethnic groups, as well as an anthropology department, be established as integral parts of the university. I explained my view of it. "Under your guidance, contributions to research made by students at the university will be extremely important. Hopefully, five to ten years from now, when having to do research on an anthropological issue, we will find that the School of Humanities can provide us with valuable monographs written by Vietnamese authors."

Mr. Trung appeared very concerned with the students' suggestion and projected many difficulties one could anticipate. The initiative could not come from him when the government as well as his colleagues isolated him, regarding him a leftist and opposition intellectual. All he could do was struggle with his own individual efforts.

That evening I stayed with Mr. Trung in the living quarters reserved for university professors in an area of Hue called Bến Ngự, or "the Royal Landing Stage." A window in his apartment on the third floor overlooked Bến Ngự river, a river dug as a canal during the reign of Emperor Minh Mang, from 1820 to 1841. On the other side of the bridge, the sloping Nam Giao Road sunk into the dark of night. This two-kilometer-long road led to the Nam Giao Esplanade, the ceremonial altar where the Nguyen emperors worshiped heaven on lunar new year. In fact, the road took its name from this altar. Around me, the monotonous buzz of insects, the sound of river frogs snapping at mosquitoes, and their subdued rhythm of life triggered memories of sorrowful pages of history.

How could one nurture one's strong will in such a melancholy milieu, so as to evolve into a superior mind like that of monk Pháp Viên? This puzzlement reminded me of the idea of resigned tolerance inherent to Hue men, as bitterly perceived by Như Nguyện. I now thought of her with longing and hope. Once again in my mind appeared the luminous face of Như Nguyện against a very dark background. In the future, when I came here to live in an apartment like this one, would the dear skylark fold her wings to spend happy days by my side? In the meantime, contemplating the somber quiet atmosphere of Hue, I fervently hoped it would inspire me to return to painting.

In a room where books and newspapers were stacked in utter confusion, I asked Mr. Trung, "Why didn't you bring your wife up here with you? The caring hands of a woman would make life more comfortable."

"That's true, of course," he answered. "The only trouble is, I am teaching at many places and am not quite settled in here as yet. Moreover, my wife must care for our young child and cannot move around easily. She wants to arrange to live in Saigon permanently. If I had many regrets in life, one of them would be that I married early."

Mr. Trung's talk gave me the impression that he did not have a happy family life. Respecting his privacy, I did not pursue the matter further.

Pouring hot coffee into white porcelain cups, Mr. Trung continued. "Lately, my mind seems to be stagnant. Because of that, my writing no longer flows easily. Reading back over what I have written, I find the words dry and dull. I should have realized this earlier and stopped at that point. Everything has to be reexamined and reevaluated from the beginning, if one hopes to find new directions."

In the eyes of young students, Mr. Trung was an idol, or a committed intellectual, to use his own terms. Even so, he was not above doubt and disappointment. He was lonely in the adoration of others. With his bright and sad eyes seen through glasses with thick lenses, Mr. Trung looked isolated, a dark solitary figure in an impoverished space. I wanted to drag him out of the deep depressed mood he had arrived at while talking about a group of student journalists who often criticized him. Happily, soon enough, when it came to rational consideration of circumstances, Mr. Trung never failed to keep his sharp sense of proportion.

"As I said, everything has to be reexamined and reconsidered from the beginning," he reiterated. "I see myself responsible for having initiated a force of resistance and opposition of a negative sort among the people. That kind of opposition—a means of avoiding constructive action—is precisely an obstacle to attempts at national development."

I recalled my earlier visit to the students' newspaper office. The visit informed me of a free and democratic spirit embedded in the activities of those amateurish writers and made me aware of the extent to which they were able to go in their protests. I, myself, liked these young journalists, and thought of them as catalysts for national construction.

"There is no way of knowing where a dialogue with those students will lead," said Mr. Trung. "Many times I have felt shamed by their criticism, but afterwards thought I understood them better. Besides, to me, avoidance of confrontation is a big mistake committed by their seniors. This avoiding act can be compared to an ostrich hiding its head in the sand in an attempt to escape danger. But in the end, we all have to face reality and truth."

The filtered coffee had gone cold and left a bitter taste on the tip of my tongue.

As always, Mr. Trung's voice displayed sincere eagerness. When having a heart-to-heart talk with students, it sounded as though he were carrying out an interior monologue, probably because he was, like them, struggling to find an answer for himself. There were signs of change in his standpoint; this was noticeable in subtle signals of an inclination toward entertainment of an alternative. He seemed to have lost his patience. His strength had been centered around his ideas and his writing, but recently he tended to believe more in the effectiveness of action. I thought of a parallel observation made by Kux, that the strength of Buddhism did not lie in violence, but, ironically, Buddhist followers had the tendency to be drawn to violent action.

The law professor and advisor to General Thuyet, along with his wife, stopped by for a visit. We discussed all sorts of things until midnight. When in bed, I felt tension in every muscle and weariness in my soul, so much so that I did not even want to raise a finger.

I woke up very early in the morning when mist still clung to the landscape. Noise and voices resounded by the river: women carrying their wares to market, the girls of Hue fetching water. Through the window I stared at leaves wet with dew; I secreted glances at girls in white blouses washing clothes on the river-bank, chattering cheerfully to one another, singing in low voices. From afar came toning of the bell at Từ Đàm Pagoda on Nam Giao Road, vibrations lulling the soft clouds into passivity and silencing the chirping of birds. The shimmering bell echoed from a time past, the year 1963, a time when, under Catholic President Diem's regime, this very same pagoda served as the center for the Buddhist movement to demand freedom and equality for Buddhism.

Perhaps Như Nguyện would be persuaded to come live in this city with me for awhile, in the secluded and quiet world of mausoleums and tombs, where we could again find a suitable milieu for painting and happiness.

CHAPTER EIGHTEEN

I went to Phu Bai airport, about fifteen kilometers south of Hue, and waited to board a plane to Da Nang. This aircraft finally came from Saigon, bringing with it the Buddhist patriarch. The patriarch, looking exhausted and aged, had to be helped into a car in the presence of a crowd of Buddhist followers who bowed very low in reverence as he went past them. The special reception room at the airport was decked out with Buddhist flags. A long line of vehicles stretching over a kilometer, complete with flags and banners, had been waiting to welcome and to escort the patriarch's delegation to the city. The patriarch's trip to Hue at this point, in spite of his old age and ill health, would confer a calming effect on the current state of agitation felt by the Buddhist laity. Among the line of cars I recognized vehicles of the government and of the military, all carrying the splendid five-color Buddhist flag. The sight made me think of General Thuyet's double-bind position, wherein he had to compromise with the protesting Buddhists in Hue, while at the same time obeying orders from Saigon to keep the city under control.

I was preoccupied with that thought throughout the flight to Da Nang. The purpose of my trip was twofold: I wanted to meet with the general in Da Nang after his recent difficult encounter with the Hue students, and I also had in mind a visit to a number of Thuong Civilian Irregular Defense Group camps that had been incorporated into Regional Forces–Popular Forces. I had a strong feeling that the highlands, with green valleys and rolling mountains, submerged in bright sunlight and saturated with the fragrance of wildflowers and grass, appealed to me much more than the Hue struggle that thinly spread over a few locations in the city, a subdued city that seemed never to awaken from its long sleep.

The writer-advisor informed me that General Thuyet had just gone to Saigon on urgent business. There was no indication of any serious upheaval, but there certainly was friction in the central government that demanded his mediation. The writer was no less busy without the general around, but thoughtfully he still managed to arrange many visits for me.

After a whole day going from the dry hills in the Lệ Mỹ area to the hot sand beaches of Chu Lai, I suffered from heat exhaustion. I told myself I would sit down in the evening, as was my habit, to record what I had witnessed, before I grew lazy and my mind stagnant. But, at the same time, I felt that I had never experienced such difficulty in focusing, unexpectedly losing my ability to connect with reality. So many things should be written, but where or with what image should I begin, I asked myself.

Should I start with the healthy, red, fleshy face of a lieutenant colonel named Clark, or with the pale, lead color of skin seen on a Vietnamese peasant? Should I begin with the American base camp in Chu Lai, fifty-six miles south of Da Nang, or with the Lệ Mỹ camp? The latter, a locality in Da Nang, was the landing point

for the first U.S. Marine Brigade in 1965. The name of the place
was curiously ominous: literally translated from the colloquial, Lệ
Mỹ means "tears of the Americans." Actually, both components of
its Sino-Vietnamese compound name mean "beautiful". However,
because it was one of the places where the Americans suffered a
lot of damage from the war, the local people, through a habit of
word play, saw an uncanny correlation between this dark reality
and what the name sounds like in vernacular Vietnamese, which
translates as "tears of America." And thus came their conversa-
tional dubbing of Lệ Mỹ as "tears of the Americans."

In any event, I was sure I should describe the much-altered
face of the countryside around these areas in contrast to my first
visit to them a few months before. From amongst the dried-up
trees and the fields of stagnant muddy water, villagers and their
villages had been moved to tracts of burning hot sand that heated
up both sides of sheet-iron roofs, a scorching sand where only
cacti and a type of hard, thorny plume grass could grow.

The law professor came looking for me and told me that the
general might be returning from Saigon in the late afternoon. He
would like to invite me to dinner, but before that, as a courtesy,
he wanted me to go with him to the airport to receive the general. As a journalist, I wanted all the more to see the general now,
after his trip to Saigon. Perhaps I would be lucky to extract many
hot news items from him.

Afternoon approached, casting light shadows on treetops. Far
out on the runway Phantom jets took off in pairs, throwing behind
them sparks of fire and thundering noise. Air force fighter aircraft
and gray helicopters took turns taking off and landing, creating a
zone of uproarious sound. The Caravelle, a new aircraft belonging to Vietnam Airlines, was supposed to arrive at four o'clock. It
was now four-thirty, and we, the anxious crowd, had been waiting here since three. Some foreign journalists grimaced their
impatience. So as not to waste time, they proceeded to write their

news items in a refreshment shop. On top of the low stone tables in front of them were glasses and bottles of soft drinks and wine.

I sat with three men: the law professor, the veteran journalist writer, and a well-known businessman of Hue origins. Because all of them, to a greater or lesser extent, had close relations with the General, their conversation evolved around disturbances after the students' Congress, and General Thuyet's attitude toward these disturbances. They were men who moved with the times, who had begun to energetically engage in social activities after the '63 Revolution when, in the confusing stage of transition, the role of the military was essential. This was also the reason that the intelligentsia vested themselves heavily in the ruling generals.

"To tell you the truth," the professor confessed, "I myself am not revolutionary, but I very much want to see a social revolution transpire. And that's the reason why I must help the younger generation to progress."

His words had a ring of sincerity. Notwithstanding the fact that revolution always requires a lot of hardship, the law professor wanted to maintain his lifestyle on a high social level, and as a result his social commitment bore the mark of condescension.

It was the businessman's turn to voice his thoughts. "I am very weary of politics. I am close to the general for friendship's sake, that's all. I have no ulterior motive whatsoever."

As if to prove his weariness of politics, in the next breath he passionately proceeded to recount the torture and imprisonment he had at times experienced during the nine years of the Diem regime. At that time, he was accused of engaging in economic and financial enterprises for the communist side, but he maintained that in reality he was doing all that for the sake of a non-communist social revolution.

"It's still frightening," concluded the businessman, "to recall being tortured by the secret police. I was lucky not to be killed by them. Come to think about it, being alive now to reflect on the near death then gives me a feeling of pleasure."

That he was among the select few who benefited immensely from the revolution which Diem's overthrow constituted must be the greatest pleasure the businessman enjoyed, I mused.

Though showing no symptoms of narcotic withdrawal for lack of opium, the writer did not contribute much to this discussion. It was hard to deny that his literary style was abundant with alluring vital sap. He often said that he shared with many the aim of revolution, but he was completely in disagreement with them as far as the means to that end were concerned. While his writing made him famous, his oratory turned him into a theorist, I noted.

The writer eventually voiced his opinion. "When talking about opposition, by implication we want to support something contrary to what we oppose. Frankly speaking, during President Diem's time, when we discussed anti-communism we meant to defend his democratic regime. Such a clear-cut perspective no longer exists. From the prime minister to a student, everyone talks as his own moods move him. Listen to the Young Turks' reckless, ostentatious declaration regarding the necessity of having an extremist revolution, a revolution which calls for a lot of weapons and a gorging of blood. They profess to be anti-communist, but they want to act exactly like the communists. What kind of righteous struggle is that?"

It was commonly thought that revolution had to involve fire and had to be energized. The writer, on the other hand, apparently came to the revolution with a cool heart. People thought of him as a member of the older generation. On the contrary, he did not consider himself among the age group to be forgotten and discarded from consideration; rather, he wanted to progress side by side with the younger generation. After all, he possessed a store of experiences in resistance against the French and the communists.

He made a decisive statement: "Communism is no longer viable. At this point, it is not necessary to prove that fact, as it is self-evident. But our present struggle must have something fundamental to hang on, no mere hook. Focusing exclusively on the idea of opposition does not automatically provide us with a righteous cause. What I want to say is, it's time we return to our ultimate homeland."

Old people share the tendency of talking much about their past. The writer differed from his friends and contemporaries on this point. Like young people, he preferred thinking about and discussing the future.

For a minute, I was rather preoccupied watching eagerly anxious faces and imagining the joy of those who had gone outside near the runway and were waiting to welcome and shake hands with the general. Sensing that the writer had directed his discussion toward me, I halfheartedly offered a response. "It's true that Marx and Lenin are no longer around to see that they were wrong. A world community only exists in utopia. Any worthy righteous struggle has to be directed toward a homeland. There is no such thing as international communism; there is only Chinese communism or Russian communism. To return to one's homeland is no other than to return to one's national boundaries."

The writer reacted strongly against my words, which contradicted his ideas. "No, that's not what I meant," he exclaimed. "I am talking about returning to a *homeland of cells*, the microcosm. Only physiologists, who observe with their microscopes the operation of these microcosmic forms of life, have the requisite authority to determine their significance vis-à-vis the macrocosmic universe."

His statement made me realize that the person engaging in this dialogue with me was not only a writer, but also a person very well read in physiology. I had to admit that his language exhibited something bewitchingly attractive, which explained why he won the general's trust and respect.

The writer continued in a lower voice. "I have great ambition. My endeavor is geared not simply toward solving small national problems on a short-term basis, but also toward what concerns the future of humanity as a whole."

Unexpectedly, in the midst of soaring on his own ambition, the writer jerked as if startled, and his voice faltered. "On second thought, national affairs alone are already too big, beyond our reach. I only have enough energy left to talk, not to act. I tried hard to publish a newspaper through which to say important things, only to have it closed down."

He stopped in silent bitterness, without any gesture of protest, as if his energy had dissipated completely. He was a curious type of individual, having enough of the bitterness of an aged person and more than enough of the superficiality and naivete of a youth. He had lived under various regimes and had experienced honor and humiliation, ascent and descent in his journalistic career. Immediately after the '63 Revolution, he honestly and sincerely confessed having prostituted his pen during the previous regime, and expressed his gratitude to the military coup for giving journalists a chance to be human again. He was a better person than his contemporary friends because of that courage to tell a dark truth, and telling the truth itself constituted the power of written words. Perhaps that was the reason that the government was weary of him and found a way to shut down his newspaper.

The writer believed that only Central Vietnam, specifically the city of Hue, was the authentic homeland of revolution and journalism. That belief explained why he had chosen to leave his family behind in the south while he lay down exhaling opium smoke in this ancient capital, performing the inconsequential role of an advisor and living colorless days of waiting for better things, better times. His youthful appearance was regarded as a bridge connecting the old and the new generations, between which the distance was palpable during this historical period of tremendous social change.

The Caravelle aircraft of Air Vietnam landed. Soon, the professor came back to our table to inform the rest of our group that the general had not returned this evening as planned, because the big meeting of the Council of Generals in Saigon at the last minute was extended for a few more days. The four of us got in the car to drive back to the city. I sat in the back seat with the writer. The other two, in the front seat, continued their discussion on the issue of the reform of the government, even as the writer started his conversation with me by explaining his own assessment of the social situation and of leading political figures.

"All nationalist politicians are the same," commented the writer, directing his gaze toward the back of the law professor's head. "Look at the professor: he loves to talk about struggling for liberation. But how? He himself has not got hold of a concept of nationalism suitable to the times and the people. He has engaged in social struggle from many standpoints, not having definitely focused on any one of them. The danger for him is precisely the tendency to change his position easily."

On any subject, the writer never failed to turn the direction of discussion to himself. "As for me, after being released from prison, not only do I distrust politics, I also loathe it. In my opinion, the only thing worth considering is a revolution, a fundamental radical revolution."

Surprisingly, contrary to his usual demeanor as a man who did not talk much, this evening the writer revealed his feelings to a great extent. No matter what issue he touched upon, he never failed to open up for me distant and immense horizons. Once again, I found his language bewitchingly enticing. I tended to think that his oratory was all he had possession of, a faculty that he had cultivated through years of living in the north.

He was some sort of impenetrable and spreading darkness. Between him and life at present there existed contradictions, and a very bizarre gap.

The next day, the professor came to let me know that the general had just returned to Da Nang—earlier than anticipated. That evening, the businessman threw a party in honor of the general. The number of invited guests was small and restricted mostly to those close to the general. In spite of that, the professor said that if I wanted, he would take me along. I accepted his invitation, even though I had grown very tired after another day of traveling around.

The party was an attempt to duplicate the world of ostentatious elegance and luxury in Saigon, and transplant it into a huge room at Trung Uong Hotel: warm candlelight, wine served in crystal glasses, roses in full bloom placed upon pure white napkins. After a few short hurried meetings with the general in the past, this was the first time that I actually had a chance to leisurely and closely observe the physical appearance of this person who was thought to exert major influence on events in the highlands. He was tall and big, but his size belied his rather amiable and soft disposition, certainly not as stern as people thought. On his low forehead was a hollow where a bullet had hit. Many sharp lines and angles defined his face, which often shifted its expressions. Most striking were his very white and even teeth, exposed often by his wide and winning smile.

Looking toward the professor, the general said, "How about it, Professor? I heard that up in Hue they are planning to go on strike again, is that correct? Your students always create disturbances there."

The professor tried his best to explain away the trouble by saying that it was not really a matter of concern, as there was no longer any legitimate reason for continued unrest. "General," he said, "I once told you that among the students there are several pro-communist elements, but I am sure you know more than I do. To restore order, you have to have all these elements arrested."

I was surprised at the professor's request that his own students be detained. As for the general, he was so gratified with this petition that he bestowed a big smile on the professor. "Professor, don't worry about that. I was able to suppress even the blood-thirsty barbaric savages, so these minor disturbances are not worth serious consideration. To arrest these students or not is simply a matter of timing. Moreover, as of now, I do not wish to create any disquietude in the people's psyche."

After a short pause, the general continued in a confidential tone. "Representing the standpoint of the government, when I have to talk to the press, I always express my opposition to revolt and unrest. But at the same time I take on for myself responsibilities of a citizen keen on freedom and democracy, and as such there is no reason for me to suppress them and not allow them to go on with their struggle. Furthermore, formerly, I was a struggle-oriented student myself, perhaps even more ardent than any of them today."

The general was quite cheerful this evening. His voice took on a tender tone when he recalled his past embroiled in struggle, especially the days of danger and difficulties he had experienced in the highlands. Then, in a sudden turn of direction, his voice became hard when the present was brought into the picture. "Listen, Professor," he said, "please relay the message that I am very lenient with the dear students, but once they allow themselves to be taken advantage of by the communists, I won't hesitate to use harsh measures. Mark my forewarning, for if things go that way, not only will I crush their struggle movement, but also have some of them shot to make an example."

The general possessed all the strong traits of a military person: an imposing stature, hot temper, and impulsive responses.

He was one of the young generals who were credited with great service to the revolution, and at present he was surrounded by a host of advisors, to say nothing of the American military advisors. The majority of his Vietnamese advisors included intellectuals, journalists, university professors, and also specialists in one thing or another. All these people saw themselves as excellent strategists, who came with their own differential mind-sets and ambitions to volunteer their services to the general, and, evidently thanks to their presence, the general had made discernable progress. From a less-educated military man, he had reached a point where he could engage in a relatively smooth discourse on different *isms* and revolution. He consistently ascribed to the military a historical mission in the two revolutions he envisioned for the future. The general also did not neglect the area of culture. At a certain meeting, which he felt had just the right environment, he even went so far as to try discussing human existence through contemporary intellectual representations, those after the fashion of Sartre and Camus. He liked Camus best. The reason given for this preference sounded similar to the viewpoint expressed by the writer, his very close friend.

This evening the general drank and talked a lot. The few strangers present, like myself, found ourselves included in his circle of friends to whom he was amiable. Taking advantage of this favorable circumstance, I struck up a conversation by asking him about war and revolution. He mentioned Nasser quite a bit, and eagerly discussed the two revolutions essential for our society at present. When going a little deeper into the reasoning, the general's standpoint proved to be hazy, inconsistent. At one point he definitely stated he believed in the necessary presence of a hero, a *strongman;* at another, he indicated an inclination to support the ranks of youths and students, and praised the struggle for freedom and democracy. Seemingly sensitive to my puzzlement, the

veteran writer-advisor attempted to point out that in the general's
view there were no strange contradictions at all. "Wholesome
revolution," he said, "is the ultimate aim, and, of course, there are
many paths leading to it."

It was not clear to me along what path the writer himself had
chosen to move in order to achieve that aim. What was clear was
that, in his writings related to this question, there was revealed an
entanglement of contradictions. He was an elderly fighter, a fighter with thirty or forty years of struggling for freedom and democracy, including freedom of the press. Yet, it was he who called for
the appearance of a dictator, and likewise it was he who had drafted a neat contingency plan to close down many newspapers and
to restrict freedom of the press. In this respect, he was in the same
league with the professor who, having fought elbow to elbow
with the students against dictatorship in order to build freedom
and democracy and to defend university autonomy, turned around
to ask the general to arrest the students who opposed people of
different viewpoints.

And I now came to realize where the general's dilemma lay:
he had overcome the difficulty of gathering many advisors
around him, but he lacked an eye sharp enough to make the right
selection among them. Consequently, the general demonstrated
his patriotism with equal passion in contradictory policies.
People expected much more from him, a talented military man,
strong like an elephant and hardworking as a buffalo. Ironically,
he was one without skill in politics, one who had been forced by
social circumstances into roles unsuitable, roles in which he felt
discombobulated.

In a voice full of intimacy and trust, the general directed his
gaze toward the professor. "The Saigon government is planning a
reshuffle and they have asked for my opinion. If that actually
comes to pass, I have the intention of inviting you to take charge
of the Ministry of Youth Affairs."

Though the general said this in a low voice, it was still over-heard by the writer and the businessman, who expressed surprise. The professor himself, taking a minute to suppress his excite-ment, answered in a cool indifferent tone of voice. "Dear General, to tell the truth, I love teaching and never wish to be away from the students. Moreover, if I left, what would the Law School have to offer? I do not like politics, and have participated in it because of circumstances, that's all. I also think that at this point not much can be achieved. But, if push comes to shove, I will accept the job only when you agree to become the prime minister, General."

The favor bestowed was so cleverly and flatteringly acknowl-edged that the general was extremely delighted. He continued in the same sweet and confidential way. "Actually, the Americans themselves perceived the messy situation in Saigon, so they sounded me out. To tell you the truth, they are weary of me and don't like me much after a few nasty concessions they had to make in the highlands. But they also understand that my role is essential, so they have flirted with me. I agree with you, Professor, that the time is not right. Let them fight and compete with one another down there for a while longer. It will take only an instant when the right time comes for me to act."

The businessman smiled his no-comment smile, while the writer quietly nodded a few times in complete agreement. At this point, waiters brought out and placed in the middle of our table a roasted piglet—crispy, browned, and smelling delicious. A half-Chinese man followed behind them, babbling something unintelligible.

The businessman turned to me and explained. "That man is the manager of this hotel. He has just won the contract to manage all clubs at airports, including that at Tan Son Nhat airport in Saigon. That's why he is so happy, and very grateful for the gen-eral's support."

"Mind you," the businessman added, "he is a top chef. You can search all over Saigon and you won't find any place with better food."

The dishes were prepared the Chinese way, and the most sumptuous banquets could not have offered more—from abalone to bird's nests, to cite but two. Everyone began to partake of the feast. The pork skin crackled sharply in our mouths.

All of a sudden, the general looked toward the minister of transportation. "Well now, Mr. Minister," he said, "does the central government intend to starve us up here? Not even one-third of the five thousand bags of rice meant for last month have yet come to us, while we are about to use up the rice in our stocks. Is there something wrong in Saigon?"

The minister, very young for such a post, was one of the general's protégés. He said that the matter, since it was connected with central Vietnam, about which he was particularly concerned, had been managed smoothly in Saigon. But upon arriving up here, he had been surprised to see this problem, now mentioned by the general. He had thought it might have been a consequence of the scandal of maritime shipping to I Corps. The scandal involved various forms of corruption that delayed the transport of goods to the northernmost provinces of central Vietnam by ship—as the war had made travel by land completely insecure. What was even more terrible was that some portion of the shipped rice cargo was stolen to be sold to the VC.

"Some among you will have to be shot before things are settled," the general admonished. "It's another stealing operation, that I will bet you. Listen closely: I task you to have the matter resolved between the time you return to Saigon and before the month is out. Otherwise, you all will not be at peace with me."

The general did not hide his pride, albeit in a sad manner, about the busy nature of his position, of his irreplaceability. "Up here, we are dealing with one serious problem after another, the

'Return to Home Village' operation after a flood evacuation, for instance, to say nothing of the nonsensical religious issue. I work myself to death here, while things remain messy down in Saigon. I am beginning to feel disgusted with everything. Adding to that, ever since I left the Central Highlands, the savages have revolted there repeatedly."

Surrounded by many advisors, the general nonetheless appeared alone. In good humor, the press often dubbed him the hero of "a solitary room"—an idiomatic expression alluding to the lonely situation of an unmarried woman, or a woman whose husband has gone away. The fact that the general had remained a bachelor up to the present moment was a mystery that provoked the imagination of many people.

The wine had the effect of calming him down, and let loose his words. "During these last seventeen months," the general confided, "I wished to have a completely free day to spend on a deserted beach where I could sit and leisurely drink a very cold glass of beer without having to be bothered by anything. But up until now, my wish has remained that, a wish."

Indeed, this evening the general showed himself a poetic soul, free from his normal fierce behavior, a behavior characterized by curses and orders to shoot people.

Among us, an old doctor had kept his silence throughout the dinner discussion. He chose this moment to offer encouragement to the general. "Incidentally, General, the refugee evacuation project in our area is being well handled. We are confronted with the very messy matter of relief supply, but, fortunately, I am used to negotiating with the Americans, so you don't have to be concerned about it."

Dragged back to the present, the general immediately became as enthusiastic as his position called for. "Really, Doctor? It is such a very big project that the Americans have suggested that a Ministry of Refugee Affairs be established. If you can make that project run as smoothly as the last flood evacuation, that will be good enough. I can't ask for more."

The doctor laughed gleefully, quite gratified. "I can guarantee that. You don't need to be concerned. Seeing that our resettlement program was being well carried out, waves of villagers have come to the refugee camps. The Americans were surprised at this outcome and asked me about it. I told them that one of our lieutenant colonels said that wherever the military operation proceeded, many people rushed to our units and begged to be taken along to a camp. But truly, evacuation of villagers is an exhausting affair, even more exhausting than fighting the VC."

Had I not known well enough about this doctor, I would have admired him tremendously. But the truth of the matter was the reverse of what he said he had accomplished. I had to restrain myself from telling the general that the evacuated villagers were being baked on stretches of hot sand and were being fed with garbage discarded by American soldiers. I also could not bluntly describe the desperation of villagers who forced themselves to follow soldiers simply because they wanted to flee for their lives before their villages were designated as being in a free-fire zone.

The doctor continued in his slimy voice. "Given this momentum, only another two weeks will see the number of evacuees exceed the government's ability to provide for them, even with the wholehearted contribution of the American army. Our winning of the hearts and minds ironically has become a burden to our side, but we can't possibly send the villagers back to our enemy. Therefore, I have become so bold as to be drafting a strategic plan which I will submit to you, General. I have considered it thoroughly, and my idea is to let the people return to their villages where they themselves will participate in defending their own communities, with the support of the central government."

The general was overjoyed with this news of victory in the battle for people's hearts and minds. He was even more pleased by the doctor's farsighted consideration of the problem. As for me, I was doubtful about the effectiveness of the flood-relief-like short-term strategy that the general had apparently come to consider as the ultimate solution. While the general turned his attention back to the professor, the businessman showed he was very much in agreement with the doctor.

"Great," the businessman declared. "When the Ministry of Refugee Affairs is established, who else but you should be the minister?"

The writer leisurely cast his eyes around the table to check on each and every face of those who might be considered by the general as candidates for one or another position. Slightly lifting a corner of his mouth, he laughed a brief laugh with the noble air of a philosopher. I glanced at the general, whose face took on a softened, peaceful expression. The strong wine, a lot of it, made me a little drunk. Faces before me were enlarged, entangled, and dreamlike. I suddenly thought of Như Nguyện, who compared herself to a little bird fleeing from snow, and visualized a painting I would paint of her, a nude woman luxuriating in the warmth of a pink carpet.

CHAPTER NINETEEN

It was another regrettable coincidence, as explained away by the U.S. Department of State, when thirty American Green Berets arrived in Argentina to establish a training camp for the government's army, only to be confronted with exposure in a Buenos Aires newspaper called *Garceta,* which pointed out that before this thirty, other groups of American Green Berets had appeared along the borders of Tucuman Province where they secretly trained antigovernment rebels. The spokesman for the State Department acknowledged only that a group of advisors had been dispatched, and did not say a word about the Argentine government's recent arrest of thirteen rebellious fighters associated with the Green Berets.

The writer-advisor expressed surprise at these rather irreconcilable facts, which made no sense to him. For myself, on the other hand, a news item like that carried a lot of meaning, for it was no less than written evidence shedding light on the actual role of American Special Forces in the Central Highlands. A "regrettable coincidence" was a term used by the U.S. State Department as a palatable explanation for hard-to-explain happenings of such contradictory nature. Sending Green Beret troops as advisors to the military of a foreign government, while at the same time helping subversive elements topple that government, was a U.S. move in a big card game where it hid an ace up its sleeve. When the deception was not easily detected, that might be a cunningly clever scheme. As for General Thuyet, notwithstanding his being firm and tough, he was not fully aware of this sort of double-dealing.

In the meantime, it looked like the general was not quite successful at incorporating the CIDG into the chain of command of the regular army within his area of responsibility. A Vietnamese regular army officer advisor to the Regional Forces–Popular Forces had been killed, and the general had yielded to pressure to replace him with a Vietnamese Special Forces A-Team. The most evident mark of failure was the shrinking number of CIDG troops, the majority of whom were Thuong soldiers; and this was obvious immediately after the order was issued to have them assimilated into Regional Forces–Popular Forces. Except for a few commanding members, who agreed to stay with a view to being promoted to the ranks of officers, the remaining Thuong soldiers who had not deserted became dispirited and weary. Besides the material aspect of their standard of living, which was quite poor in comparison to what they had enjoyed previously while living in American Special Forces camps side by side with the American Green Berets, these Thuong soldiers were haunted by their experience of being mistreated by Vietnamese officers. From that feeling of distrust, sooner or later, one after another, they would leave. Their destination would not be the deep jungles where they would be isolated, but the welcoming arms of the American Special Forces in numerous border camps.

The general might or might not know about this, but it was certain that he did not have a farsighted view founded on the basics, or he would have grown concerned. His apparent strong action, including the way he dealt with the Americans, originated from self-esteem, from the practice of face-saving that was valued by Asians, more than from a carefully considered plan. Even a sharp thinker like the writer, his close advisor, was not astute enough to correctly assess the importance of events in the highlands. The general's main objective seemed centered on a reshuffle of the Saigon government and on finding a way to maintain peace and harmony with Buddhist leaders. Looking around, I failed to identify even one ally who would rekindle concern for the troubled highlands. Indeed, the tragedy of Dakto, with its more than six hundred dead bodies, had been relegated to oblivion.

I returned to Saigon with a feeling of being let down. This might be because there was such a big gap between the legendary image and the real person of the general. My feeling about this might also have resulted from a realization that the general's political role had been overestimated, whereas, in essence, he was simply a leading general, a talented military man in the proper sense of the term. However, in spite of that, I still believed that his possible return to the highlands promised good things to come.

This optimistic view did not help change the fact that I was quite exhausted both physically and mentally after this trip. I planned to take the weekend off and go to the beach by myself in order to restore my health and to find myself again, find that self which seemed to have been sucked unwittingly into so many historic events. Indeed, as things turned out at this point, I was confronted with a circumstance unfortunate for an artist like myself, an artist in an unsettled state of mind, faced with having to make a choice between staying on in journalism and quitting it. The cause of this dilemma was a deadly psychological blow that at first prompted me, out of weakness, to opt for the second alternative. It came in the less-than-creditable form of an anonymous letter, but one with a very brief and decisive message. It was possible—in fact I was almost certain—that it came from the communist front that wanted to forestall an unfavorable psychological effect following the Dakto massacre, which my pen might evoke. It would be less than honest to say that I had no fear when being labeled anti-revolutionary and threatened with death. And this was so very ironic, because my writing had also once been accused by the director of the Military Security Service of being like that of a communist who would stab the ARVN in the back and weaken the nationalists' fighting spirit!

The reality of the present stared me in the face: I was being strongly condemned by the communists. When I decided to pick up my pen to write only exactly what I witnessed or heard firsthand, I had been well aware that danger would come from many directions, a complication that would make it impossible to identify the real enemy. I was equally disheartened to contemplate the possibility that I might not be accepted by those Thuong people whose ultimate aim was peaceful coexistence and progress, much less by the separatists. Many times Như Nguyện had reiterated her observation that my single individual effort would not amount to anything in face of the present devastating situation, and if I was to be killed—which was all the more likely now—this effort would have been proved absurd and futile. Moreover, she insisted that since I was essentially an artist, it only made sense that I returned to painting, my real native world and natural occupation.

I wished I had not entered this tiring and dangerous occupation of a journalist. But at the same time I could not conceive of returning to the world of painting as a way of escaping from my current perilous circumstance. So terrible was the present feeling of isolation, of being rejected by society! But at the same time, one also felt that being solitary was itself that which promoted one's growth. This consideration instantly helped reassure me, so that I was again ready to continue with my chosen path, even if I might fall. Without any challenge, I argued to myself, a time would soon come when life appeared colorless and dull—*et soudain je m'aperçois que je n'ai aucune raison de vivre*—when I would suddenly become aware that I had no reason to live.

I did not like that dark vision. Rather, in the midst of a limited life span within this impermanent universe, the prospect of an impending mishap in the future made me feel more drawn to life and the acts of living it. I thought of Như Nguyện, of my family and relatives, and especially of my old mother, whom, for some reason, I had not dearly missed until now. Thereupon, I made up my mind to visit her, very much in the same way a spoiled impious child in repentance returned to his family.

When I stepped into the house, my mother was deeply engrossed in reading the book entitled *Tâm và Thức của Đạo Phật,* "True Mind and Deluded Mind in Buddhism,"

I silently sat down in a chair nearby.

After a minute, it came to me as a painful shock that her hair had turned completely white. How long had it been that I was away from life here and from my mother before I recognized such a change in her appearance? And since when, since how many years back in time, had she been sitting there, in the same chair covered with brown leather, surrounded by familiar objects frozen in their allotted locations?

The image of her evoked a feeling of peacefulness mixed with a touch of sorrow. Looking at her dry, thin fingers, I felt tears welling in my eyes. I wanted to be able to embrace and kiss her on her forehead, bury my face in her chest, and hold her hands, those hands that had bestowed love and tenderness throughout my childhood. But the air, filled with religious devotion and asceticism, held me back. It felt like a distance had sprung up that withered the comfort and intimacy of the mother-child relationship, and the voice of love and care was reduced to a silence of heartrending reflection.

My mother was still alive, but far from this world of attachments. I could no longer hope to find again that gentle, kind mother of my memories. And correspondingly, it would seem definite that my own heartlessness and neglect in years past had killed the last rays of longing in her. My repentance could in no way restore such a big loss.

It was perhaps the first time I spent a night without sleep, growing anxious about the condition of my bone-dry eyes staring at darkness. I had to wait until the curfew was over the next morning before going downtown.

Luxurious Saigon was still in its slumber, so the pure and fresh air of the early hours helped calm my heart somewhat. Vans transporting foodstuffs from the outskirts had arrived in the city. From my home to the newspaper's office, I was stopped and checked twice by the security police. Even though I showed them my press card, flashlights were directed fully into my face, while I had to raise both arms into the position of one about to be executed. That associated thought sent a chill down my spine. Yet, here I was, already more than a year in journalism, with all its customary and expected frictions.

Recently, because of very strict censorship, I lost my appetite for news hunting on my own, and contented myself with reports from VNTTX, the government's Vietnam News Agency. I had to sacrifice a lot of initiative. Furthermore, exactly as the editor-in-chief wanted, for awhile now, I had limited myself to describing events objectively, with neither comments nor personal impressions added. On the other hand, it was precisely difficulties and even danger that had initially attracted me to journalism, and at present I did not think I could easily abandon this poor and disordered area of city life for a return to the brush and the easel.

This morning I planned to go to work at the paper's office as usual and to keep to myself the threat in the anonymous letter that had frightened me quite a bit. I was aware that the couple of trips I had made to Da Nang-Hue did not actually bring any practical benefits to the paper; but knowing that I wanted to go, the editor had not said anything to prevent me. Such treatment toward an employed reporter like myself—as opposed to a freelance journalist—could be considered rather special. Even though there was a big gap between us, both in terms of age and of seniority in our career, our relations were always a blend of warm friendship and mutual respect. His anxious expression upon seeing me, which he made no attempt to hide, told me that he had been waiting to see me. The first sentence he uttered was contrived with a forced touch of humor by way of creating a calm and relaxing air.

"Your spirit seems to cast a dead spell on our newspaper! The Ministry of Information has sent their warning for a second time in less than a month."

I had not expected that my writing would actually bring such troublesome threats to the paper and its employees. At the moment, I felt like casting considerable blame upon myself.

"If it had not been for their consideration for me personally," the editor continued, "this paper would certainly have been closed down. But the matter has not ended there. You, yourself, author of the article, must meet with the Minister of Information to answer a number of questions. The issue seems to have touched various ministries, and caused anger to the prime minister, because of the severe criticism voiced by superior monk Pháp Viên as reported in your article. Each ministry has a complete copy of the translation of that five-thousand-word article teletyped from Mr. Davis's office. The Minister of Foreign Affairs blamed it all on the Minister of Information. Given the circumstance, it is you, not me, who has the responsibility to explain the facts."

I had thought that after my interview at the office of the Military Security Service this matter had been completely resolved and settled. But evidently I was far from free of the consequences of that five-thousand-word article. I knew only too well that, with regard to a figure as well-respected and very much in opposition as was monk Pháp Viên, the government's policy was to isolate him and drop him into the void of public memory. My crime was thus defined as going against the government's line, by highlighting the monk's presence. It was judged that my article had the effect of heavily embellishing the person and the legend of monk Pháp Viên, particularly so in the mind of American and European people.

Fully aware of my impatience and high self-esteem, the editor took care to advise me to show my goodwill by presenting myself at the Ministry of Information immediately. He thought it would serve me best if I displayed an obliging attitude as an indirect way of acknowledging my mistake, just as months ago the paper had admitted its mistake in publishing reports on events in the highlands, which publication the authorities attributed to our intention to cause problems for the government. I paid no mind and placed no value on accusations of that nature, when I had decided for myself that my sole responsibility was to the readers for what I published in the paper.

My eventual meeting with the minister of information was such a dull affair. It bore nothing approximating the provocative excitement that had characterized my previous encounter with the director of the Military Security Service. The minister's face was ordinary, his voice artificial. The interview, above all, was quite vapid, especially when once again in my journalistic career I had to listen to banal reiteration of writers' and journalists' responsibilities in connection with social situations of the time. His approach was very ambivalent. At one point, in the name of a colleague, he confided his own thoughts; at another, he asserted his responsibility and authority in controlling the information machine of the government during wartime. Whatever came out of his mouth, in the end, focused on the threat of taking me to court or having the secret police interrogate me for the crime that he called jumping over censorship and abetting the foreign press in undermining national security.

I grew tired, really tired at this point. My almost numb calmness and lack of response surprised him. Certainly he was wise enough not to create a press scandal from which he could not emerge with righteousness and fame. At the last moment, he apparently decided to change his tactics. Doing away with intimidation, and offering promises of material rewards, he attempted to persuade me to collaborate. The final touch came when, for the first time during the interview, he surprised me by mentioning that he knew my name was included in the list of the press delegation soon to visit six foreign countries. In a subtle way, albeit clear enough for me to understand, he said that if I was allowed to join this overseas journey, it would be because of his goodwill in intervening, as the Ministry of Foreign Affairs had already voiced its objection.

CHAPTER TWENTY

Even though the morning sun had not completely dissolved a layer of cold mist, already I was present at the airport to join General Tri's delegation to the ceremony that would mark transfer of Daksut Camp, north of Dakto, from American to Vietnamese command. Two helicopters lifted up, carried us away from two mushroom clouds of thick red dust, and headed straight in the northwest direction. After many days and months, this was the first time that my vision was no longer restricted to the confines of a narrow and cramped room: it expanded to embrace high mountains and long rivers.

Because of an "accident," which could be called an occupational hazard, I had been hospitalized in the highlands for six months. In the same incident, Davis had been mortally wounded by a bullet through his head and died while being evacuated. For six months, I lived in the hospital bed like an outsider, struggling in solitary with the excruciating pain from my wounds and receiving no word from Như Nguyện. Her neglect evoked longing in my heart and sharpened the realization that my skylark had spread her wings to fly high so as to abandon the past, which lay behind her as though it had never existed. I had tried to save my soul from dejection by immersing myself in intellectual pursuits and in intensive writing.

Six months were long enough a time for a conjuncture of events to affect and change the whole complexion of the country. Echo of the turmoil in the highlands seemed to have sunk deeply into oblivion, and it became a thing of the past. It looked like all the opposing sides in the conflict had finally come to realize that it would give them not an iota of benefit to continue with that game, so filled with blood and tears. In addition, the dawn of real revolution, more than once promised by General Thuyet, was far more removed from actualization when the "internal correction affair" of another military faction took place, resulting in exile from the country of three generals, including General Thuyet himself.

Meanwhile, on the other side of the Pacific Ocean, there was a sharp divide in political viewpoints. The American people had lost their patience with the Vietnam War, and they began to split into contending factions. The Americans, while successful in predicting the day when they would set foot on the moon, got bogged down in the earthy Far East. One way or another, sooner or later, the Vietnam War, itself, would have to wither. That thought was no more than a momentary consolation in face of mounting agitation among the American public. The hope of ending the war was far from becoming a reality when every day the United States still added fuel to the conflict in the form of billions of dollars and of thousands of tons of weapons, and when divisions of North Vietnamese soldiers, in defiance of American B-52 bombers, day and night poured down along the Ho Chi Minh Trail to continue their infiltration into the South.

From another angle, when the conflict had gone past the guerrilla warfare stage, when Hanoi had switched to confronting the Americans openly right in cities and towns, secret schemes to exploit the bloody racial separation in the highlands were no longer of sufficient strategic value to deserve continued support. That was, perhaps, the reason for the ready and smooth transfer of American Special Forces bases along the borders to the command of the local authorities. The transfer was part of the American plan for an honorable withdrawal, which went by the designation of Vietnamization of the war.

Leaving the high section of a river flowing over hill and dale, the helicopters changed direction and flew due north. The Americans surely had enough of the toxic defoliant, Agent Orange, to lay in ruin all the immense jungles spreading beneath us. Groves of trees, stripped of leaves, displayed white tops and looked very much like heads of gray hair. Life down there was breathing its last breaths. The sky lowered and rain flew among damp cold clouds. The uncovered parts of my body became numb.

After thirty minutes in the air, the helicopters began to descend and circled around, changing direction. The camp, occupying the whole top of a hill amidst surrounding valleys, was encircled by many defensive barriers. It was equipped with 105mm artillery pieces, and an airstrip designed for the C-123 Caribou—a Short-Take-Off-and-Landing-type aircraft—to land and deliver supplies brought to the high-riding camp from the lowlands. Not far from the airstrip were two hamlets, one for Kinh people and the other for Thuong people, where houses with corrugated metal roofs clustered very close to one another. This was the ninth American Special Forces camp to have been established, and it was considered the most important among a total of sixty-two in the whole of South Vietnam, because it served as a solid barricade to check infiltration of North Vietnamese communists from Laos. This very morning it would be handed over to a Vietnamese Special Forces A-Team. Subsequently, the twelve American Green Berets constituting the American Special Forces A-Team, A243, would board two awaiting helicopters and leave forever this camp, a camp that their efforts had made as solid as a fortress during the eight years since they had ventured to set foot on this mountainous spot, a location completely without security and quite deserted.

Of importance was the fact that precisely at this place, four years ago, a massacre of Vietnamese had occurred, which, in the aftermath, led to repeated racially induced bloodshed. That devastating event had been a thorn stuck in General Thuyet's throat. Had he remained in Vietnam, this day would have been one of the happiest of his life, much as, in contrast, it had to be a dark and bitter time for Tacelosky and the American Green Berets, a day that only added to their difficult straits and somber demeanor. Ever since President Kennedy, the father who had created them, was assassinated, this strong and brave combat arm had been confronted with numerous difficulties and had been stripped of all its special privileges.

On the other hand, this day offered General Tri a good opportunity to assert his role in the highlands. Right at the beginning of the speech delivered at this ceremony, he was wise enough, as he had always tried to be in his position, to highly extol the effective support given by the Americans in general and by the members of American Special Forces Team, A243, in particular. This great support was expressed in their joint effort with the Vietnamese to transform the wilderness of the locale into a strong military base, which helped both Kinh and Thuong peoples to have a comfortable life and to progress in all aspects. The general went on to say that he strongly believed that, with the continued support of the United States, and, given all the experience they had gathered in years past, teams of Vietnamese Special Forces would be able to assume direct responsibility for management and control of all Thuong Civilian Irregular Defense Group camps.

The hand-over ceremony was conducted with full formal ritual. As a line of honor guards saluted, the head of the American Special Forces A-Team handed over the camp's standard to his Vietnamese counterpart. Both smiled and gave each other a firm handshake. Subsequently, on behalf of his team, Captain Cobb, the American leader, originally from Owellsboro, Kentucky, took the floor and expressed their impressions at the point of departure from this camp.

In a voice lightly shaken with emotion, the captain spoke in fluent Vietnamese. "We're very sad, and we find it very hard to part from this camp, where for years American and Vietnamese Special Forces have labored and shared hard work with Kinh and Thuong Mike Force units to construct infrastructure and develop a security system in order to protect the lives of approximately six thousand people. Those people came from neighboring areas to settle in hamlets built near the camp's encircling belts of defense. But, at the same time, I must also say that we're very happy to witness the beginning of peaceful coexistence, and close cooperation, between ethnic Vietnamese and ethnic minorities, with a view to building together a modernized Vietnamese nation."

It was obvious that his opening remarks conformed well to diplomatic protocol, the same protocol that made it inadvisable for him to bring up his true concerns about Kinh-Thuong antagonism still haunting him, and especially his detection of signs of protest from pro-American Thuong leaders, which had appeared from the initial stage of Vietnamization of local CIDG camps.

As soon as the captain finished his last statement, the military band played the special Green Beret march while Mike Force teams, looking fierce in their leopard-skin-patterned camouflage fatigues, marched past the review stand. And subsequently, like many times before, Vietnamese officials once again were forced to witness the ritual of buffalo sacrifice by which Thuong Mike Force units took an oath of loyalty to the government of South Vietnam. At the camp's central command post, the American flag was slowly lowered; then a Vietnamese flag was raised in perfect timing with the strongly accentuated beat of the familiar national anthem.

While guiding the press representatives to the two hamlets for observation, Captain Cobb proved to be well-versed in a few Thuong languages as well, when he cheerfully greeted and talked to elder tribesmen and their descendants. Filthy half-naked children, instead of shying away in fear, rushed to circle their arms around his legs, played and ran about him happily, as if they had known him intimately. An American reporter raised a question about the feeling of insecurity the Thuong people might have upon seeing the Americans depart. The captain admitted that this was indeed an issue.

"However," Captain Cobb added, "up to the present, sympathy of the people has been with our side. They've had bitter experiences with the communists. Moreover, they would not be foolish enough to go back to the deep jungles and end up suffering from hunger and being shot at by both sides. That was also considered by MACV as solid a reason as any to hand over to the government of South Vietnam all inland and border camps."

Additional information was supplied by a black sergeant named Wynne, a veteran Green Beret from Texas, who had been at this camp since he first set foot in Vietnam. To Wynne's understanding, the common view held by many people was that the camp was valuable as a solid and fortified military base whose function was to prevent infiltration of the enemy. But, in his opinion, the truth went beyond that, as the ultimate mission of the camp was quite political. It had to do with the campaign to win hearts and minds, and thereby to entice people to the Saigon government's side.

To end his explanation, with a smile the sergeant leaned down to lift up and embrace a grimy-faced little girl. "The villagers," he said, "do not want to see us leave, but unfortunately that was the decision taken by our higher authorities, and it is also the wish of the Saigon government."

A few seconds passed, then Wynne added in a sorrowful voice: "How sad to be a Montagnard."

I mentioned General Thuyet's name in connection with the future of the highlands. Wynne did not hide a bitterness in his tone of voice when he responded, "Had he not left the country, today would have been the happiest of days regarding his dream of creating a kingdom."

I also talked with Raphael, an American sergeant who was the senior Special Forces medic, whom the villagers addressed as Doctor. Though without Wynne's bitterness, this man also showed his sad feelings. "My long stay here has made me very attached to this place. Departing today, I feel as if I am leaving my second home."

Interestingly, also during this ceremony, I ran into one of the amateur student journalists whom I had met a few years ago when we both followed and reported on the development of the FULRO revolt in the highlands. He had graduated from medical school and no longer engaged in journalism. At present he was the chief physician of a Vietnamese Special Forces C-Team. He joked that his choice to serve here was perhaps due to his karmic relation with the Thuong. But I knew that to an idealistic person like him, the choice was a commitment to what, as a student, he had believed in and enthusiastically advocated.

He told me of his present assignment. "My current responsibility is to take charge of healthcare for all CIDG camps. However, generally speaking, supplies and logistic support still depend heavily on the Americans."

It was really incredible to me that all the issues that had yesterday been so very much the cause of severe conflict among different sides suddenly had disappeared and were no longer of any significance. I asked the doctor what he thought were the factors that helped bring about the apparently stable situation in the highlands at present. In a calm manner—this was a change I noticed in him since we last met—he offered a rather sharp observation.

"To arrive at the compromise that we see today, they had help from experiences gathered over many years now past—by 'they' I mean the Americans. Truly, their experience taught them that to take a hand in the Thuong's rebellious schemes does nothing but further tarnish their name, and in no way helps improve their present lamentable standing. But the more important factor is that both Kinh and Thuong peoples, after so much bloodshed, have come to clearly realize that given the correlation of their fates by which the action of either side affects the life of the other—*môi hở răng lạnh*, 'when your lips part your teeth get cold' as we Vietnamese say—they have no better choice than to come close together and join hands in building a new collective nation of Vietnam."

Though I myself had seen signs of some positive changes, I was not as overoptimistic as he was. And perhaps Major Y Ksor was correct when maintaining that to transform into reality the vision of the highlands as a Promised Land was a task that would take "longer than raising a cup of rice wine to your lips"—as a Thuong idiomatic expression goes—a long and arduous task entailing much more blood, sweat, and tears.

—Bunard Camp, 1969
Delta 49